LAS AMERICAS PUBLISHING COMPANY
152 East 23rd Street, New York 10, N. Y.

QUEVEDO

THE SCAVENGER

Translated into English and with an introduction
by Hugh A. Harter

Title: THE SCAVENGER

Author: FRANCISCO DE QUEVEDO

Translator: HUGH A. HARTER

Illustrator: ADOLFO HALTY

First Printing, May 1962

Original Spanish Title
EL BUSCON

Printed in the United States of America
by COCCE PRESS

TABLE OF CONTENTS

· THE SCAVENGER

5

FOREWORD

This new English version of *The Scavenger* will, hopefully, introduce to many American readers a work which is almost unknown in this country except to those who have made a special study of Spanish literature. Notwithstanding this, Quevedo, the author of the work, is a humorist and satirist of the stature of Rabelais and Swift, to whom he has frequently been compared, and in the annals of his own land ranks second only to Cervantes himself.

The Scavenger, it is generally conceded, is one of the best examples of the picaresque novel ever written. It serves as an excellent introduction to the genius and virtuosity of Quevedo, who is, for the Spaniard, the prototype of the mordant satirist and wit. The descriptions of human foibles and of the life and times which fill the pages of the book give a vivid and memorable picture of Spain's decline and fall from her dominant position of power and glory. Furthermore, Quevedo's astounding mastery of his native tongue, his unique gifts for caricature and comedy, his fundamental stoicism before the cruelty and corruption of his times and his penetrating powers of observation are nowhere more apparent than in this extraordinary novel.

The first English translations—published under various titles— were made in the seventeenth century. Editions also appeared in French, Italian, Portuguese, Dutch and German. The English versions have not, on the whole, been satisfactory. Some have been pastiches of earlier translations; some are exceedingly cumbersome and permit the reader only the dimmest of glimpses of the vigor and forcefulness of the original. Style is consistently sacrificed to content. The result has been that the brilliance of author and book alike have been rendered prosaic and uninteresting.

The present edition is designed to remedy this. It furnishes the American public an English version which reproduces as fully as possible the style and content of the original. It may be read and enjoyed for and by itself or in conjunction with the reading of the Spanish original. The Spanish edition which was used is the version edited by Professor Américo Castro, first published in 1927 and now made available again in the Clásicos Castellanos series.

The translator's introduction which precedes the body of the work presupposes that the American reader will have little acquaintance with either the author or his times. Consequently it provides, we hope, a discussion which will make a first encounter with Quevedo a significant one.

I should like to express my gratitude to Professors Lida and Gilman of Harvard University, and to the late Professor Claude E. Anibal of Ohio State University, for their help and encouragement of the present translation, and to my *compadre*, Adolfo Halty, for his excellent illustrations for this edition.

Hugh A. Harter
Chatham College, 1962

INTRODUCTION FOR THE AMERICAN READER

FRANCISCO DE QUEVEDO Y VILLEGAS

The author of the *Buscón—The Scavenger,* as we have Englished it—was born in Madrid in the year 1580. His family, which was of the aristocracy, came from the region of La Montaña near Santander in northern Spain. The father was secretary to Anne of Austria, the fourth wife of Philip the Second; the mother was one of the queen's ladies-in-waiting.

The father died while Quevedo was still quite young, the mother was occupied with her duties at Court, and the future author was therefore put in the care of a tutor. This plus the fact that he was both lame and nearsighted undoubtedly contributed to the cynicism and bitterness which color all of his works, even the most humorous. His studies became, whether by choice or by necessity, a refuge for him.

At the age of twelve he became a student at a Jesuit school, and at sixteen went off to the University of Alcalá de Henares, at that time one of the great European centers of learning. During the years at Alcalá these became clearly apparent: an outstanding facility with languages, an amazing memory, and a startling and caustic wit. He mastered Greek, Latin, Hebrew, Arabic, French, and Italian. He took degrees in philosophy and theology, and his knowledge in these fields, as well as in civil and canon law, medicine, and even mathematics and astronomy places him in the forefront as one of the most erudite of his compatriots. He began writing in these years too, and acquired a European reputation as a scholar, as evidenced by his correspondence with the celebrated Belgian, Lipsius.

Various anecdotes have come down to us about Quevedo's life as a student. They tell us of brawls and bawdy houses, duels and pranks, and it would seem that Don Francisco was equally at home in the environment of bohemians and picaros, or in the company of scholars, writers, and courtiers. The chapters in *The Scavenger* on hazing and student life in general at Alcalá are undoubtedly drawn largely from experience, and we may make the supposition that Quevedo himself was the originator of the pranks which Pablos tells of with such obvious pride and delight.

9

After taking his degrees, the young author became attached to the court, which in 1601 moved to Valladolid. He remained there until 1606, when Madrid again became the capital. During these years he was already becoming known as a writer. His portrayal in brilliant and biting satire of the vices, follies, and injustices of his times in the *Visions*, the first of which date from 1606 or 1607, and *The Scavenger*, which literary historians now generally date from 1608, indicate that he was very carefully observing the life of the glittering but corrupt and decadent court. He alone was clearly cognizant of the weaknesses and abuses of the powerful, and their vices and extravagances at a time when only leaders of Spartan virtue could have saved the country from the ever-increasing poverty and idleness.

In addition to gaining a reputation as author and wit, Quevedo was also making both enemies and friends. Among the former was the famous swordsman, Luis Pacheco Narvaez, who earlier had published a book on the art of dueling. The anecdote of the meeting between the two men appears to be founded on fact, and is the basis for the episodes with the fencing master in Chapter VIII of *The Scavenger*. Both authors were, it seems, guests at the home of a nobleman. Quevedo stated certain disagreements with theories of swordsmanship that the latter had included in his book. Pacheco, whose pride had been hurt, challenged his critic to a fencing match in which, despite the handicaps of being lame and nearsighted, Don Francisco won. Pacheco never forgave him.

Among the friends acquired in this period, the most important one is Pedro Téllez Girón, the Duke of Osuna, who became the Spanish viceroy of Sicily in 1610. At the Duke's invitation Quevedo made his first trip to Italy in 1611. His voyage has long been ascribed to a legendary duel over an unknown woman in which Quevedo killed his adversary. The tale, for all its frequent repetition, is probably not true.

The trip does mark the beginning of a long period of participation in Italian political affairs. After a brief return to Spain and a stay at his country estate of La Torre de Juan Abad, he returned to Sicily in 1613 and assumed the roles of Osuna's prime minister, ambassador, and entertainer for the rest of the decade.

Quevedo's career as ambassador of the viceroy was an impressive one. It frequently led him into dangerous and colorful situations. He played an important role in the settling of the war in Lombardy and in 1615 made the first of two important trips as emissary to Philip the Third, ostensibly to present the King with monetary contributions and to discuss the conduct of certain af-

10

fairs in Sicily but actually for the purpose of obtaining, by means of enormous bribes and gifts to the highest officials of the court and by intrigue, the post of Viceroy of Naples for Osuna. Quevedo fully justified his patron's confidence in him. He also impressed the King enough to obtain, on this occasion, the granting of a pension, and two years later, the coveted knighthood in the Order of Santiago.

By 1617 the long-standing rivalry between Spain and the Republic of Venice for predominance in the Italian peninsula had reached dangerous proportions. It led to the famous "conjuración de Venecia," a plot in which Quevedo played one of the principal roles. He was even in Venice when the projected overthrow of the Venetian Republic was discovered. He escaped with his life only because of his fluent Italian and a beggar's disguise.

The failure of the Spaniards and the consequent embarrassment to the Spanish government were not, of course, without their repercussions. Not even the efforts of Quevedo could avert disaster for Osuna, who, in 1620, returned to Spain in disgrace and was imprisoned. With the death of Philip the Third and the accession of Philip the Fourth, things became even worse. Quevedo himself was confined on his estate and banned from entering Madrid. By 1623, however, he was exonerated and returned to the precarious life of the court. The Count-Duke of Olivares, the Favorite of Philip the Fourth who was for all purposes the real ruler of Spain, showed the author his favor for some time. Olivares' good will was not to be counted on for too long, however. Quevedo was temporarily banished from the court in 1628. He married in 1634, but lived with his wife only three months.

Five years later, in 1639, he was accused of being the author of a poem attacking governmental abuses and corruption, a copy of which was placed under the King's dinner napkin. The result was that Quevedo was summarily imprisoned for a period of four years. He might well have finished out his life in prison had not Olivares, in his turn, fallen from power in 1643. Quevedo was released, but he was ill and broken by the terrible experience of his imprisonment. He spent the last months of his life in his Torre de Juan Abad, and died in September, 1645.

Despite the ups and downs of the years after the return from Italy, Quevedo saw published his most famous and important works. Some, like *The Scavenger*, had been written earlier, and others, like his serious politico-philosophical works *La vida de Marco Bruto* and *La política de Dios*, date from this period. He was a tremendously versatile author as the general list of his works at the end of this introduction indicates. He wrote theological, philosophical, and po-

11

litico-ethical works, polemics and literary criticisms, novels and sat-
ires; he made translations of classical authors and the Bible; he
also wrote plays, but these, unfortunately, have not come down to
us. He is classed with Lope de Vega and Góngora as one of the
three greatest poets of his age. As we have said, his countrymen
rank him second only to Cervantes as a satirist and humorist. In a
period which saw on the contemporary scene such artistic giants as
Cervantes, Lope, Tirso, Velázquez, and Murillo—both of the latter
painted portraits of the author—Quevedo stands out for the breadth
of his interests, the extent and depth of his culture, and for his
amazing wit and ability with language. He was the sharpest observer of his times, and one of the greatest stylists and most versatile
and complex writers of Spanish literature.

The Scavenger

The picaresque novel as literary form dates its beginnings
from the publication of the Spanish *Lazarillo de Tormes* in 1554.
It appeared at a time when idealistic and poetic tastes dominated the
literary scene. The most widely read narrative form in the first
half of the sixteenth century was the novel of chivalry, and in the
second half, the vogue of the pastoral novel begins.

Both of the latter types are escapism. The knight-hero, while
at the same time satisfying the appetite of the reading public for
fantastic adventures, was the embodiment of the Humanistic idealism of the Renaissance. He was noble in both blood and spirit. Virtuous, valiant, and invincible, he set out on his adventures and travels motivated by the ideals of love, honor, and glory. His outward
appearance, the shining armor, the plumes, and the richness of
his costume, was the external evidence of this nobility and purity
of heart.

The pastoral novel is more aristocratic in its appeal and more
artificial in its expression than the novel of chivalry. Whereas the
latter idealized the warrior, the pastoral form represents the ideal-
ization of nature, and an analysis, highly artificial for the most part,
of the sentiments and amorous passions of shepherds and shep-
herdesses whose rustic costumes are frequently disguises for the true
identities of persons in court circles. The Moorish novel, which also
enjoyed a vogue in the sixteenth century, represents some of the
best aspects of both the other predominant forms, while at the same
time avoiding their excesses.

It was the picaresque form of the novel that was, however, to
prove the most fruitful and lasting. The genre spread throughout

Europe and to the New World, becoming, through the works of such authors as Lesage, Fielding, Sterne, and more recently of a Mark Twain or a Thomas Mann, a vital part of the tradition of the contemporary novel. In contrast to the idealistic genres it largely superseded, it is often described as realistic. The term is not wholly accurate, however, as recent Spanish scholarship has pointed out. The realism of the picaresque is not the purported photographic reproduction in literary form of contemporary life, as is claimed by nineteenth-century novelists, for example. It does, nevertheless, include many scenes—the Spaniards call this type of descriptive art *costumbrismo*—of custom, costume, and manners of the everyday life of the people. Also, it relies on concrete details in the building of its comic scenes, and this, as well, has helped earn it the label of "realistic," even in those passages which are largely drawn from literary or folkloristic sources.

The Lazarillo and its literary descendants constitute a counterpart to the idealistic novels and present a radically different point of view. Noble and lofty idealism disappears. The values of the novel of chivalry—which shares in common with the picaresque its wide acceptance by the public—are, so to speak, reversed. The knight is now a picaro; the hero, an anti-hero. His princely parents are replaced by a father who is a thief and a mother who is a witch or an adulteress, or both, as in *The Scavenger*. The armor and rich costume have given way to rags and tatters.

The same transformation occurs in the realm of values. The knight's search for fame and glory through feats of daring and bravery finds in its place the exaltation of personality, hollow bluster and boasting, and empty gesture. Responsibility and dedication to ideals are superseded by necessity and hunger. Love is reduced to sexual desire. The picaro's story is not one of privilege, pride, and achievement as is the knight's; it is one of privation and struggle to attain a certain virtuosity in what are usually the rather dubious arts of survival in a society which has made him an outcast.

Although the form and content of the *Lazarillo* were not definitive, the essential ingredients of the picaresque genre were there. The protagonist, a picaro, tells his story in the form of an autobiographical narration, starting with a tongue-in-cheek description of his birth, parents, and rearing, and passing on to the satirical portrayal of the social levels and types he encounters on his travels from town to town and from roadside inn to roadside inn in search of menial tasks by which to sustain life. Both epithets that are applied to the form, "epic of hunger" and "epic of the road" are fittingly descriptive. The adventures which Lazarillo encounters as

13

he moves about are related as separate and distinct stories and scenes which are loosely held together by the autobiographical form and by thematic material and style. In the humorous and satirical tone of the telling and the portrayal of a series of low moral and social elements—in *The Scavenger*, the courtship episode which we shall discuss further on is an exception—the book is all of a piece.

The *Lazarillo* remained an isolated phenomenon for some time, however. It was not until the very end of the century, with the appearance of Mateo Alemán's *Guzmán de Alfarache* in 1599, that the picaresque genre really came into its own. From that point on it dominated the field of Spanish fiction for half a century.

The *Guzmán* is more extensive than its predecessor. Its protagonist is much more peripatetic than Lazarillo. His travels carry him along road and through city in both Spain and Italy. He enters and describes a highly diversified series of social groups ranging from beggars to noblemen and from thieves to prelates of the Church. In addition to the autobiographical narration of the adventures of the picaro, there are long didactic passages which moralize on the experiences of the hero; there are also interpolated short novels of different types—as, for example, in the first book of the *Quixote*— and other elements not an actual part of Guzman's life.

With the *Guzmán,* the picaresque novel took on a definitive form, including the observation of the contemporary scene, satire, and moralizing. It recognized the aesthetic possibilities and values of the low and ugly, but the book is overly long and its frequent sermonizings are tedious. Furthermore, despite comic scenes and episodes, its tone is consistently bitter and pessimistic.

The Scavenger contains elements found in both the *Lazarillo* and the *Guzmán*. It follows the mock autobiographical pattern. Pablos, the protagonist who narrates his life, is the picaresque anti-hero whose characteristics we have outlined above. He starts out in life as the servant of a master, but like the more complex Guzmán, moves in many and diverse social levels and backgrounds. The first phase of the novel, the descriptions of Pablos' educational experiences, both the formal ones and those of the school of life, are considerably more lengthy than in either of the earlier novels. On the other hand, there are none of the didactic digressions of the *Guzmán,* the preaching and moralizing. Quevedo relies in *The Scavenger* on the overall effect of his picture of the life of his times to carry his political, sociological, and ethical message. He has also greatly intensified the tone of pessimism, and at the same time, has heightened the comic effects. He has, as would be expected of a man of such a breadth of interests—often contradictory—, given us a book which is both more compressed and more complex than its predecessors.

The structural outlines of the plot are relatively simple. There are twenty-three chapters in all. In most editions there is a division into two books, the second beginning with Pablos' arrival in Madrid with the destitute nobleman in Chapter XIV. We have by this time learned of his family, his education in Segovia and at Alcalá, his pranks and petty thieving at the University, and have become acquainted with some of the people he encounters on the road during his first travels. Pablos is still not a picaro, however. He first enters a truly picaresque world on his entry into Madrid where he becomes a member of a brotherhood of picaros. The destitute nobleman who acts as Pablos' mentor thus helps the relatively inexperienced youth to bridge the gap between what we might call, in contemporary terms, "amateur" and "professional" status.

The figure of the nobleman, although not as striking as that of the famous Master Cabra, is one of the most memorable in *The Scavenger*. He also participates in the life of Pablos and the action of the story longer than any of the other secondary characters. In addition to introducing Pablos into a truly picaresque world, he plays a major role in the expression of Quevedo's political and philosophical views. He is the embodiment and corporal representation of the Spain of the reigns of the last two Philips.

To the student of Spanish literature, Quevedo's nobleman immediately brings to mind the impoverished *hidalgo* of the *Lazarillo*. Appearing at the center of that novel, he represents a high point in Lazarillo's encounters. He is destitute of material goods and has only the clothes on his back, yet he maintains a sense of personal honor and pride which we, and his young servant, cannot help but respect. His honor represents an exaggerated emphasis on birth and background. It is negative to the degree that it will not permit him to better his situation by entering any useful form of occupation. On the other hand, it constitutes a positive value. He is the best of Lazarillo's masters; although he possesses the least, he is the most considerate and generous. The boundary line between servant and master is never crossed, but the two become friends and show a deep respect for each other as human beings.

To compare these two figures from the two novels can be very revealing of the differences between the two ages in which they were created. There are similarities between the two men: both are of the lesser nobility, both are penniless, and both are concerned with keeping up appearances. There the resemblance ends. Pablos' mentor has a title which is pompous and hollow. He would gladly sell it if he could, like any other external trappings. The Spanish "don," a title of respect and position roughly equivalent to the English "Sir," has been reduced to absurdity. It has no more meaning than the sound of the same syllables in any ordinary word. This seventeenth-century nobleman has none of the pride of background or of tradition his predecessor has. Both avoid useful occupation, but Quevedo's gentleman does so because he prefers the easier and freer life of the picaresque adventurer. He is equally at home in palace or prison, among beggars and thieves or the well-to-do.

Most important of all, however, he represents the widening gulf between appearance and reality. This theme is fundamental to *The Scavenger* just as it is to the *Quixote* or to Calderón de la Barca's *Life Is a Dream*. We can see this in Quevedo's constant play on words. By introducing terms which have two or more meanings in the first part of a sentence, Quevedo masks what he is saying until he resolves our doubts with a second term or phrase which is related to and clarifies the earlier word or expression. He uses this for various effects, but mostly for comedy. Language also serves to distort scenes and figures. Quevedo creates a vision of reality similar to what we see in a carnival mirror, giving us portraits which, while not photographically realistic, penetrate to the very soul of the object portrayed; Goya almost two centuries later uses this same technique in the magnificent satirical etchings of the Caprices or the somber world of the paintings of the Quinta del Sordo, and giving us, as the author himself tells us, figures like those in a painting by Bosch.

Pablos' first sight of the nobleman as he comes walking along the road is of a well-dressed and wealthy gentleman whose coach and servants, he supposes, are following him at a slower pace. The nobleman soon dispels this illusion by telling Pablos how exhausted he is from walking. The next element of surprise—and of humor— comes when Pablos gives his companion a boost to help him mount the ass. He finds that the cape which covers the gentleman's back hides a bare posterior. Even the costume is not what it appears to be. It, like the gentlemanly gestures and the title, are illusion, a clever but empty disguise which masks a sordid truth.

Pablos' mentor thus differs from his literary predecessor in several aspects. Although both men live lives of sham and pretense, their reasons for doing so are very different. One has pride in his blood and the other has none. The latter is quite as much of a picaro, in conduct and morals, as is the novice, Pablos, who is apprenticed to him. He is motivated by necessity, not a sense of personal honor, and is as much of a petty thief and cheat as any of his low-born companions. Lazarillo's master lacks will power or skill; Pablos' mentor, on the contrary is skillful and shrewd. And both are affected by economic necessity. The difference between these two literary figures of the sixteenth and seventeenth centuries lies in their attitudes to the problem. In the earlier century money and material possessions, while not disdained, were not to be confused with personal values such as honor and pride, or faith and belief, if we consider the realm of religion. By Quevedo's time this has changed completely. The emphasis is on outward show, hollow gesture, ritual, and form rather than content and meaning. Pablos' friend apes his more prosperous peers in manners and dress. So long as he can display the outward signs of pomp and wealth, he is accepted as an equal. Ostentatious living had to be maintained, whether with needle, rags, and thread, as in the case of the brotherhood in Madrid, or by the borrowings and mortgagings of even the best families, from the royal house on down.

The Scavenger contains a gallery of portraits which are conceived in a manner similar to that of the destitute nobleman. They represent a wide range of social and moral types, all embodying to some extent or other, a vice, flaw, or reprehensible aspect of the society of the times. They all partake, in varying degrees, of the seven deadly sins, pride, envy, anger, covetousness, lust, gluttony, and sloth. Vanity, pretentiousness, hypocrisy, and greed are found in all of them. It is true of all the women members of the picaresque underworld: the madams, the witches, the thieves and pilferers, and the adulteresses. Even the two ladies of the nobility, Doña Ana, whom Pablos hopes to marry, and her aunt, are not free of faults. The former is of a beauty that does not extend beyond the flesh; she is completely vapid and incapable of carrying on an intelligent conversation. The aunt is pretentious and greedy for a wellborn and wealthy husband for her nieces. The nuns have flirtations and pious women rely entirely on the counting of beads and the verbal repetition of prayer, both ritual without meaning.

The men typify an even wider range of vices. There are the addled and the superficial, smug in their pretentiousness and conceit. The poets and writers who are lampooned in the Proclamation of Chapter X and other places in *The Scavenger* fit this category, as do the armchair strategist, the fencing master, and the discharged soldiers with their tales of battles they never fought. These figures are usually handled with a sort of whimsy and a light comic touch. On the more somber side, we have the sordid deception of the father and of his death, the repulsive and scatological one of the uncle who is the hangman, of the latter's repugnant companions, of the cruel and dishonest notary, and of the brutish thugs of the last chapter. Only a master of comic techniques of the stature of Quevedo could have saved these passages from descending to the level of the purely macabre and repulsive. The author's skillful use of mock dignity, slapstick, and language make the scenes laughable, however, despite the fact that, as in much of the so-called "sick" humor and jokes current at the present time, the basic situations at which we are laughing are of a bitterly serious type.

There are also a number of figures in the book which do not belong to either one of these extremes. Their misdeeds and lack of moral sense are too great for whimsy, yet they do not fit into a category of the repugnant. The card-playing monks, the sharpers, the bribe-taking jailers, the wooers of nuns, the destitute nobleman and his friends, and finally, but not least of all, Pablos himself, fit at varying distances from the extremes into an intermediate category which lies between folly and the wholly criminal or repulsive.

As in the case of Doña Ana and her aunt, Don Diego must be considered by himself. He, like the two women, does not belong to the picaresque world. In the passages which deal with the courtship of Doña Ana, in Chapters XIX and XX, Pablos reaches his highest point and comes closest to attaining his goal of social and financial stability. In almost all of the rest of the book we find the reflection of reality recorded in the linguistic contortions of the descriptions. Here, however, in the world of the highly-born and well-to-do, the language itself becomes direct and straightforward, conveying the sense of security and well-being at this level of society, plus the mood of the idyllic moment of expectation it represents for Pablos.

Don Diego is a young gentleman who, unlike the destitute *hidalgo*, has both family and possessions. Pablos remarks, while both youths are at the University of Alcalá, that the virtues of the one made the vices of the other just that much more evident. He is, then, seemingly the only virtuous person in the novel. Even the cruel and brutal beating of Pablos for which he is responsible may to some extent be justified in view of the age's general lack of sensitivity in this respect and of our protagonist's trickery and deceitfulness regarding his intended bride. The fact is, however, that Don Diego's sin is lust. The beating which was intended for him and which Pablos receives was an act of revenge in an affair of honor involving a woman whom he had wronged. Not even Diego, then, is virtuous.

Pablos himself has both vices and virtues, weaknesses and strengths. He is a rogue like the others of his kind. He steals, lies, cheats, schemes, and exploits. He does menial jobs, begs, or struts his part whether on a street or in a play, with equal aplomb. He is amoral rather than immoral, and in all of this he is a participant in the spirit of his time. He is, in the final analysis, not much better or much worse than the others who appear in these pages. He is a very sharp observer. He has a sense of wit and humor, and is generally successful at whatever he undertakes. Consider, for example, his ingenuity and virtuosity at pranks and pilfering at Alcalá, or his evident ability as an actor and writer—the latter fitting admirably with the supposition that this narration is an autobiography.

He is, we would say today, a product of inheritance, environment, and circumstance. He starts life as an innocent and rather pathetic child who has ambitions of being something better than his parents. He ends up a rootless outcast with a prostitute as a sort of common-law wife and a group of cut-throats as companions. He has suffered physical violence and indignities. Each time he has glimpsed success, fate has intervened and he has fallen lower than before. Nevertheless, he accepts his lot with stoical determination and without complaint. He adapts rapidly to circumstances through necessity, and he learns by experience that he can rely only on himself for protection in a predatory world that is beset with dangers. When we consider all of this, Pablos, despite his obvious faults, becomes a person who merits not only our attention, but our respect and sympathy as well.

QUEVEDO'S PRINCIPAL WORKS

Quevedo's works have been published in various editions, many of which are currently available at reasonable prices. The complete works—*Obras completas*—are obtainable in the two-volume edition published by Aguilar in Madrid.

SATIRICO-MORAL WORKS
El Buscón.
Los sueños.

ASCETIC WORKS
La vida de Santo Tomás de Villanueva.
La providencia de Dios.
La vida de San Pablo.

COMMENT ON CONTEMPORARY EVENTS
Grandes anales de quince días.
El lince de Italia.
El chitón de las tarabillas.

HUMOROUS WORKS
Premáticas y aranceles generales.
Epístolas del Caballero de la Tenaza.
Capitulaciones matrimoniales.
Carta de un Cornudo a otro, intitulada El siglo del Cuerno.
Premática del tiempo.

HISTORICO-RELIGIOUS WORKS
España defendida, memorial por el patronato de España.

LITERARY CRITICISM
La aguja de navegar cultos con la receta para hacer soledades en un día.
La culta latiniparla.
El cuento de cuentos.
La Perinola.

POLITICO-PHILOSOPHICAL WORKS
La vida de Marco Bruto.
La política de Dios, gobierno de Cristo.

QUEVEDO

THE SCAVENGER

TO THE READER

I would suppose you to be, reader or listener—the blind cannot read—desirous of examining the wittiness of Pablos, a prince of the picaresque life.

You will find herein every type of knavery—most of which, I believe, are entertaining—cunning, deceit, innovations and methods born out of idleness for living by strategem, and you can profit from them no little bit if you pay attention to the lesson. While you're doing so, take advantage of the sermons, for I doubt if anyone would buy a humorous book in order to avoid the impulse of his natural depravity. But however that may be, give it the applause which it deserves. When you laugh at its jokes, praise the talent of the person who recognizes that it is more agreeable to read about the lives of picaros, described with a flair, than about things of heavier content.

You already know who the author is. You are not unaware of the price of the book since you already have it in your home—unless you are leafing through it at the bookseller's which is an annoying thing for him, and something which should be rigorously forbidden; there are those who sponge books as well as food, and the man who reads in snatches at different times pieces it all back together. It's a very sad situation that such a thing can go on because a man like that can make his criticisms without its costing him a cent, a miserable and bastardly sloth not to be encountered even in the Knight of the Sponge. May God keep you from bad books, from the police, and from blondes,[1] gold diggers, and moon-faced women.

---

[1] Blondes were considered bad luck.

CHAPTER I

THE HERO TELLS WHO HE IS
AND WHERE HE'S FROM

I, sir, am a native of Segovia. My father's name (God rest his soul in heaven) was Clemente Pablo. His reputation was known to all. He was a barber by trade but he was such a high-minded man that he usually was called a shearer of cheeks and a tailor of beards. People said he was of very good stock, and to judge from the amount that he drank it's believable enough.

He was married to Aldonza de San Pedro [Saint Peter], the daughter of Diego de San Juan [Saint John], and the granddaughter of Andrés de San Cristóbal [Saint Christopher]. People in the community suspected that Mother was not of pure Christian blood. She, however, would point out the names and surnames of her forefathers and claimed to be a direct descendant of the Litany. She was good-looking and was so widely known that during her lifetime almost every verse writer in Spain spent some time on her. Her tribulations began when she was first married and continued long after as sharp tongues declared that my father had very nimble fingers for other people's gold. It was proved against him that while he was wetting the beards of the men he was shaving and had their faces over the water basin, my little seven-year-old brother cleverly rifled their pockets. The poor little angel died of whippings in jail. My father was very upset over the loss, for the child had been a very willing thief.

For things like this and other childish pranks, Father himself was put in prison. However, as I was told afterwards, he came out of jail so honorably accoutered that he carried more red on his back than a company of cardinals, with the difference that his was not of the cloth. It's said that ladies crowded to the windows to watch him pass by, for he always cut a most handsome figure, whether on foot or on horseback. I'm not saying that to boast, for everyone knows how little conceit there is in my character.

Now my mother had no such troubles. One day an old woman who had been my nursemaid was praising her. She said that Mother

23

was so affable that she bewitched all those she dealt with. She went on to say, however, that she had heard tell something about a devil in goat's form, and flying, all of which almost brought Mother a fine set of feathers so she could do her flying in public performance. She was known for restoring maidenheads, for curing the bald and disguising grey hair. Some called her a seamstress of pleasure; others referred to her as a bone-setter of broken desires, and for a dirty name, procuress. To some she was the card in the three-card suit, but she was an ace in the hole to all the men and a straight flush after everyone's chips. To hear her jolly laugh when things like this were repeated to her was enough to make you thankful to God. I won't take time right now to tell the penance she did. All around her room, which only she could enter (except for me since I was quite small), she kept skulls which she said served as reminders of death, or perhaps, of love-spells in this life. Her bed was rigged out with hangmen's ropes, and she would say to me: "What do you think of these? I keep them as holy relics, for most hanged men are saved."

My parents had many disagreements over whose profession I was to follow, but I who had had gentlemanly inclinations from earliest childhood, applied myself to learning the trade of neither one nor the other. My father used to say to me: "Son, thieving is not a trade but a liberal art." After a pause and a sigh he would fold his hands and say: "Anyone who doesn't steal in this world doesn't survive. Why do you think cops and constables hate us so? Sometimes they run us out of town; other times they whip us, and still others they hang us without so much as respecting our Saint's day or the Sabbath. I can't talk of it for tears." The old boy would sob like a child remembering the drubbings his ribs had undergone. "All just because they don't want any other crooks around to interfere with them and their stooges. But cunning can keep us out of their clutches. In my youth I always plied the churches, and not because I was such a good Christian. Many's the time I might have avoided being whipped through the streets on an ass's back if only I had sung on the rack. I never confessed except when the Holy Mother Church required me to. Consequently, with things like that plus my profession, I've provided for your mother as well as I could." "What? You provided for me?" she exclaimed in a rage because I would not apply myself to learning with craft. "It's I who provided for you, and by my cunning got you out of jails and gave you money to spend while you were in them. If you didn't make any confessions, was it because of your courage or of the potions I brought you? It was thanks to my boxes of spells. And if I weren't afraid

24

everybody in the street would hear me, I'd tell about the time I got in through the chimney and got you out over the roof."

She was so angry she certainly would have said more if with all of her gesturing she hadn't broken her rosary whose beads were made of the teeth of the deceased she had helped. I quieted them down and told them that I was determined to learn virtuous ways and to carry out my good resolutions. Therefore I asked them to put me in school, since, without reading or writing it was impossible to do anything worthwhile. What I had said sounded sensible enough to them, although they muttered over it for a while. Then my mother busied herself at restringing the teeth, and my father went back out again—but whether for the business of beards or of purses I'm sure I don't know. I was left to myself giving thanks to the Lord for having made me the son of such astute and thoughtful parents.

Chapter II

HOW I WENT TO SCHOOL
AND WHAT HAPPENED TO ME THERE

The next day my primer had been bought and arrangements made with the schoolmaster. I went off to school. The teacher seemed happy to see me and said that I had the face of a sharp and quick-witted fellow. That morning, in order not to make him out a liar, I did my lesson very well. The teacher had me sit close to him; most days he made me monitor for being the first to arrive and for staying late to run errands for "Madame," as we called the teacher's wife. By similar helpful acts, I put them both in my debt. They began to show me too much favor, a thing which made the other boys envious. I made friends with the sons of gentlemen and important persons, and in particular with the son of Don Alonso Coronel de Zúñiga with whom I ate lunch. I went to his home on holidays and was his daily companion. The other boys, however, either because I didn't talk to them or because they thought I was too presumptuous, went around calling me names that had to do with my father's profession. Some called me Mr. Switch-Blade, and others, Mr. Swindler. One, just to hide his envy, said that he didn't like me because my mother had sucked his two little sisters' blood at night. Another chap said that my father had been brought to his house to clear out the rats, which was a way of calling him a house-breaking old tomcat. Some yelled "scat" when I went by and others "meow." Another declared: "I threw two eggplants at his mother when she wore the Inquisition's hood." They stayed right on my heels, but glory be to God for making my shoulders broad enough to bear it all. Though I was often on the run, I pretended to pay no attention to them.

I put up with it all until one day a fellow had the nerve to call me the son of a whoring old witch. Now since he had said it so clearly — and even if he hadn't it wouldn't have stopped me —, I picked up a stone and clouted him on the head. I ran off to my mother, who helped me to hide. Then I told her the whole story. When she had heard it she said to me: "Good for you. You showed the stuff you're made of. Your one mistake, however, was in not finding out from the boy who told him such things." When I heard her say that (since my mind was always full of the most noble thoughts), I turned to her and said: "Oh Mother! The only regret I have is that it was more like hearing mass than having a quarrel." She asked me why I said that, and I replied that it was because I had heard the gospel truth. I begged her to tell me if I could wipe out his lies with a dose of veracity, or to tell me if I had been begot in a quota system for many or was the son of my father alone. She laughed and answered: "Great heavens! Are you so wise already? You're not going to be anybody's fool. You have a ready wit. You did the right thing to crack open his head. Whether such things are true or whether they're not, they shouldn't be said." The words left me half dead and with my mind made up to gather quickly what belongings I could and leave home. That's how deeply shame could affect me. I pretended to overlook it all. My father patched up the boy's head and I the quarrel, so I went back to school where the teacher received me very angrily until, on hearing the cause of the scuffle, he decided I had been right and so he calmed down.

During all of this, the son of Don Alonso de Zúñiga, whose name was Don Diego, came to see me frequently. He seemed to have a sincere affection for me, for I would exchange tops with him if mine was better than his; I would give him part of my lunch and expected nothing in return; I bought little engravings for him, taught him to wrestle, played at bullfighting with him, and kept him continually entertained. So it was that almost every day, the young gentleman's parents, seeing how much he enjoyed being with me, asked my parents to let me have dinner or supper and to spend the night with him.

Now it happened that on one of the first school days after Christmas, as we were on our way through the streets, we met a man called Pontius de Aguirre, who was said to be a Jewish convert. Little Don Diego said to me: "Call him Pontius Pilate and then run away." Just to please my friend, I called the man Pontius Pilate. He turned red and started to run after me with his knife drawn to kill me. I was obliged to seek shelter in my teacher's house, screaming for help. The man followed me in, and my teacher only saved me from being killed by promising to punish me. Although the mistress took my part because I ran errands for her, she met with no success. The teacher ordered me to take down my pants, and as he whipped me said with every stroke: "Will you ever say Pontius Pilate again?" I answered: "No, sir, never." I gave the same answer twenty times, one for each stroke he gave

27

me. I had been so severely punished for saying Pontius Pilate and was so terrified that the next day when I was ordered, as was usual, to say prayers for others and got to the Creed — just notice, sir, how ingenuous I was — instead of saying: "He suffered under Pontius Pilate," and remembering that I should never again let the word Pilate pass my lips, I continued: "He suffered under Pontius de Aguirre." The teacher laughed so hard when he recognized my innocence and saw my fear that he put his arms around me and promised to pardon me from the next two whippings I brought on myself. With this decision I was really happy.

To put things briefly, our traditional carnival time was now approaching, and our teacher, to give his pupils some fun, announced a game called "King of the Roost." Twelve of us chosen by him drew lots for the honor, which, it turned out, fell to me. I asked my parents to get me a fine outfit. When the appointed day came, I sallied forth on a consumptive and withered old nag that more from lameness than from manners made a curtsy every other step. His behind looked like a monkey's and was without any hair. His neck was like a camel's, only longer. He was injured in one eye and blind in the other; in fact, he was so old all he needed to close down for good was for someone to shut both his eyes. His back looked more like a saw's than a horse's. All he needed was a scythe and he would have looked like a grim reaper for old nags. He showed abstinence in his appearance and gave evidence of fasting and penances. No doubt he had never had any acquaintance with either barley or hay. What caused the most laughter were the numerous bald spots he had on his hide; if he had had a lock on him he would have looked like a horse-hair trunk. I rode along on him swaying from side to side like a Pharisee in a Holy Week procession. The other boys in their costumes followed me (for with the greatest of majesty I rode along on the aforementioned four-legged contraption), and we passed through the square (it frightens me even to mention it). When we got as far as the stalls of the vegetable women (God help us), my horse snatched up a cabbage and quickly sent it on its way to his guts. Considering all that trip through his neck, when it might reach its destination was anyone's guess. The market women, insolent like all of their kind, began to shout. Many people gathered, including a pack of rascals who grabbed up huge carrots and fat turnips, eggplants, and other vegetables, and began to pelt me, the poor "King." Seeing that the battle was a vegetarian one and that my mount would want to stay where the shots flew thickest, I began to dimount. Just then a chance missile hit my horse so hard a blow in the face that he reared up desperately and we both fell — pardon my frank speech — into an open privy. You can imagine the state I found myself in! By this time my subjects had armed themselves with stones. They were attacking the stall-keepers and had managed to break open some skulls. For my own part, after my fall into the outhouse, I was the most diSTINCtive person in the fray. The police arrived on the scene and began questioning people. They arrested both stallkeepers and boys, searching them all for weapons and taking away what arms they found. You see, some of the boys had carried daggers and small swords as part of their costume. Then they got to me, and seeing that I had no arms, as I had taken them off and put them in a nearby house, they kept asking me where they were. I answered that except for being offensive to the nose, I was without any defense. In passing I forgot to tell you, sir, that when the market women began to hurl egg-plants and turnips at me, I got the idea, as I was wearing a hat covered with plumes, that they had mistaken me for my mother, and that they were pelting her as they had done often before. Being young and innocent, I cried out: "Sisters, although I'm wearing feathers I'm not Aldonza de San Pedro, my mother," as though they couldn't tell the difference from my clothes and my face. My fear and the suddenness of the occurrence may help to excuse my stupidity. But, to get back to the sheriff: he wanted to take me off to jail but couldn't because he could find no spot clean enough to get hold of me, I was that covered with filth. After that, some went one way and some another. I went straight home from the square, bringing martyrdom to as many noses as I came near to along the way. I went into the house and told my parents what had happened. They became so furious at seeing me arrive in such a condition that they were ready to beat me. I lay the blame on the drawn-out and worn-out old nag. I tried to calm them down, but nothing would do. I left the house and went to see what had happened to my friend Don Diego. I found him in bed with a bad bump on his head because of which his parents decided not to send him to the school any more. There I also got news of my horse who, finding himself hard-pressed, had got up enough energy to give a couple of kicks, but was so feeble that he threw his hip-joints out of place in the attempt and then lay half dying there in the filth.

Therefore, since the holiday was ruined, the whole town scandalized, my parents all upset, my friend with an injured head, and my horse dead, I decided not to return to the school nor to my home, but to stay on as a servant to Don Diego, or to put it another way, as his companion, an arrangement which would surely please

30

his parents because of what my friendship meant to the boy. I wrote home that there was no need for me to attend the school any longer because, although I still had not learned to write well, for my intention to make a gentleman of myself, the primary requirement was to write badly. Consequently, I gave up school to save my parents that expense and left home to spare them any more grief. I informed them where and how I was, and that I would not see them again unless they gave me special permission to do so.

CHAPTER III

HOW I WENT TO BOARDING SCHOOL
AS DON DIEGO'S SERVANT

As a result, Don Alonso decided to put his son in a boarding school. One reason was to wean him away from the luxuries of home, and the other was to save himself the burden of looking after the boy. He had heard that in Segovia there was a teacher of good educational background named Cabra [Goat] who specialized in the training of the sons of wealthy families. Therefore he sent his boy there with me along as his companion and servant. It was the first Sunday after Lent that we fell into the clutches of perpetual hunger, for such misery as we found in that school could not possibly be exaggerated. Cabra was a tubiform clergyman, liberal only in height and having a small head and bright red hair (no more explanation need be given) [to anyone knowing the old saying, "Neither cat nor dog of that color is any good."] His eyes were set so deep in his head that he looked like a man peering up out of two caves; they were so sunken and dark they would have made ideal places of business for shady merchants. His nose, which had once been a Roman one, had been worn flat by sores, from *colds*, but which one would have thought to come from the French disease except that *that* illness involves the price of a girl. His beard had turned pale from fear of his mouth which seemed to threaten to make a meal of its neighbor. As for his teeth, I don't know how many were missing. I came to the conclusion that they must have been sent off into exile for sloth and indolence. His throat was as long as an ostrich's, with an Adam's apple so protruding that it looked as though pure necessity had forced it to start out searching for food. His arms were withered and his hands were like two bundles of twigs. From the waist down he had the appearance of a fork or of a compass. He had two slender legs and he walked very slowly. If anything upset him, his bones rattled like the clappers leprous beggars use. His speaking voice was hollow. His beard was full because he never got a trim (to avoid spending money). He said that seeing the hands of a barber fiddling around his face made him so nervous that he'd rather die than let someone give him a

32

shave. One of us students cut his hair. On sunny days he wore a cap; it was riddled with holes and had a trimming of grease. His cassock was such a wondrous thing that no one could tell just what color it was. Some, seeing that it had no nap on it, concluded that it was made of frog skin. Others said that it was an optical illusion; from near at hand it appeared black while from a distance it was a sort of dark blue. He wore it without a belt and it had neither collar nor cuffs. With his long hair and his shabby cassock, he looked like Death's own personal servant. Each shoe could have been a Goliath's coffin. And his room? There were not even spiders in it. He put spells on the rats for fear they might eat up a few miserable crumbs he had hoarded. His bed was on the floor and he slept always on only one side of it in order not to wear out the sheets. In short, he was the archetype of poverty and the quintessence of avarice.

I fell then into this man's hands, and in his power both Don Diego and I lived. On the night we arrived he showed us to our room and made us a speech which he kept very brief so as to make no expenditure, not even of time. He told us what tasks we were assigned and these kept us busy until time for our dinner. We went in to the table. The young masters ate first, and we servants waited on them. The refectory was a room the size of a half-peck measure, but up to five could be seated at the table. The first thing, I began to look around for cats. When I didn't see any I asked one of the older servants, whose thinness was the brand of his boarding school life, why there weren't any. He began to look sad and said: "What do you mean, cats? Who ever told you cats liked fasting and penance? You can surely see from the fat on you that you're new here." When I heard this, I commenced to lose heart. I was even more frightened when I noted that all those who had lived in the place for a while were as thin as awls with faces that looked as though they had been powdered with flour. Headmaster Cabra sat down and said grace. Then the group ate a meal that was essentially eternal: it had neither beginning nor end. Waiters brought in soup in wooden bowls. They were filled with a broth so clear that Narcissus would have run more danger eating from one of them than in drinking from a fountain. I watched how greedily the withered hands plunged after the orphaned and solitary pea at the bottom of the bowl. With every sip Cabra would exclaim: "Say what you will, there's nothing like a stew. All the rest is vice and gluttony." After he had had his say, he would down the rest of his bowl and exclaim: "Good for the health and better yet for the mind." "The devil take your mind!" I thought to myself when I

caught sight of a servant half ghost and so thin that the platter of meat he carried looked as if it had been picked off his own bones. On the platter was one adventurous turnip, at the sight of which the teacher said: "Turnips, eh? There's not a partridge that can compare with them. Eat well, for I'm always pleased to see you eat." He apportioned each such a tiny piece of mutton that, with what stuck to their nails and was lodged in their teeth, it seemed every shred was consumed, leaving the stomach cut off from its share. Cabra looked at them and said: "Eat well, for you're growing boys and I delight in seeing your hearty appetites." Imagine, sir, what seasoning that provided for a group of youngsters who were yawning from hunger.

When dinner was over there were a few crumbs left on the table and some scraps of skin and bones on a plate. The master said: "We'll leave that for the servants. They have to eat too. Let's not take it all for ourselves." "The Lord curse you and all of your food, you old devil," said I, "for the threats you have made to my stomach." He said the blessings and then went on: "Well now, let's make way for the servants. You boys run on and get some exercise until two. That way your meal will digest properly." I couldn't hold back a hearty laugh any longer mouth wide-open. The teacher got very mad at this and told me I should learn decorum. Then after quoting three or four old proverbs he left.

We all sat down. I could see that things weren't going too well. My stomach was roaring for justice, and as I was healthier and stronger than the others, I launched an attack on the plate and the others followed suit. I crammed two of the three crumbs and one scrap of skin into my mouth. The others began to shout. Hearing the noise, Cabra came back in and said: "Eat like brothers, for the good Lord has given the wherewithal. Don't quarrel, for there's enough for all." He went back out to sit in the sun and left us alone. You may believe me, sir, when I tell you that one of the fellows whose name was Jurre, a Biscayan, had so completely forgotten the how and the where of eating that two different times he lifted the bite-sized food he got as his share up to his eyes, and on a third try still couldn't hit on the way to his mouth. I asked for something to drink, a thing the others, because of their almost continuous fasting, never did. I was given a glass with some water in it, and had hardly put it up to my mouth when, as if I were a communion lavatory, the ghost-like boy I mentioned before took it away. I rose from the table with a heavy heart for I realized that I was in a house where toasts to the health of one's guts were proposed, but nobody drank. I felt a desire to ease nature, that is to say

35

to relieve myself, even though I hadn't eaten. I therefore asked one old man where to satisfy my needs. He answered me that "since no one has any such need in this house, there is nowhere to go. For the one time you have to relieve yourself while you're here, any place you can find will do. I've already been here two months and I haven't done such a thing since the day I arrived, just like you now, because I had eaten at home the night before." How can I tell you the gloom and the pain that I felt? It was so great that when I considered how little food my body would get, I didn't dare, even though I felt a strong urge, to part with a thing.

We kept very busy until nightfall. Don Diego asked me what he could do to persuade his innards that they had had food, for they flatly refused to believe it. Dizziness reigned in that house just as indigestion did in most others. The supper hour arrived (afternoon snacks drew a blank) ; we ate even less, and instead of mutton, had teacher's namesake to eat: roasted old goat. Only the devil, sir, could have invented anything that bad. "It's very healthy," Cabra remarked, "to eat little so as not to overwork the stomach." Then he quoted a whole string of hellish physicians. He sang the praises of dieting and said it keeps people from having bad dreams. He knew full well that the only dreams possible in that house were ones about food. They ate and we all ate and yet none of us ate.

When we went to bed, neither Don Diego nor I could sleep a wink, he for planning to complain to his father and ask him to take him away from such a place and I for urging him to do so. At last I said to him: "Sir, are you sure we're both still alive? Because I have a feeling we were killed in that battle of the market-place and that we're souls in Purgatory. That way it won't do any good for your father to take us out of here unless someone does a lot of praying for our sins and gets us out of our misery at some very special altar."

With these discussions and the little that we slept, the hour to get up soon arrived. Six o'clock rang, and Cabra called us to our lessons. We all went to class to hear recitations. I bared my teeth which were covered with tartar and yellow with despair. I was called on to read the first part of the lesson, and my hunger was so over-powering that I ate half my words and so had my breakfast. Anyone who heard the story Cabra's servant told me can easily believe all this. He said that when he first came there, he saw two great

36

work horses brought into the place, and that two days later they left, so light that they flew off through the air. He also declared that he saw two massive watchdogs come in and two greyhound racers make their departure three hours later. One Lent, he went on, he noticed a crowd of people. Some were thrusting their hands, some their feet, and others their whole bodies into the entranceway. This went on for quite a while, some people coming from places some distance away. Finally Cabra got so angry that he asked what they were doing there. One man explained that some had the itch and others chilblains, and that by entering that house all the illnesses were starved out. Not even disease could thrive there. The servant swore it was true. Knowing the house I believe it. I'm telling it now so that no one will think what I've described was just exaggeration. But to get back to the recitation: Cabra made the assignments and we learned them by heart. Life went on in much the same old way. The one and only change was the addition of bacon to the stew because of something said to Cabra about being of pure Christian blood. As a result, he took a little metal container which was perforated like a salt shaker, opened it, and filled it up with bacon. Then after closing it up tight, he dangled it by a string into the stew so that some of the flavor would ooze through the holes. He would then pull it back out so that he bacon remained for the following days' use. Afterwards he decided that this expense was too great, and from then on he only waved the bacon over the top of the stew.

You can picture the life we led. Don Diego and I were about at the end of our rope. Since we could find no remedy for our lack of food, we tried to get some relief by staying in bed, and we said we were ill. We didn't dare say that we had a fever because that would have been too easy to check on; a headache or toothache weren't serious enough. Finally we said that we had cramps in the stomach caused by three days of constipation. We knew that in order not to have to spend a cent for medicine, Cabra would make no hunt for remedies. But the devil ordained otherwise, and he dug up an old enema syringe that had been left to him by his father who had been a druggist. He diagnosed our trouble, took up the syringe, and prepared the medicine. After that he sent for his seventy-year-old aunt who acted as nurse. He told her to give us each a good enema. They began with Don Diego. The poor chap was bent over and the old woman, instead of making a proper injection, discharged the dose between his shirt and his backbone as far up as his neck. What should have been a lining on the inside served to trim the whole outside. The poor boy began to yell. Cabra came in and seeing him said to give me the other dose, that they would get back to Don Diego later. I resisted, but it did me little good. While Cabra and some servants held me down, the old hag pumped me full. I promptly gave it all back, straight in her face. Cabra really lost his temper and said that he would throw me out of his house, for it was clear to see that our illness was just a scurvy trick. I prayed to God that he would expel me, but needless to say, I didn't have that much luck.

We complained to Don Diego's father, but the Old Goat persuaded him that we had planned our stunt to avoid doing our lessons. With that our prayers came to nothing. Cabra brought in the old lady to do the cooking and to wait on the boarders. He fired the servant because one Friday morning he had found some crumbs on his clothing. What we went through with that old hag God alone knows. She was so deaf we had to scream at the top of our lungs, and she was almost completely blind. She was always saying her prayers, and one day her rosary broke over the kettle of stew. She brought in the best blessed soup that I ever ate. Some of my companions exclaimed: "These must be black peas from Ethiopia." Others said: "Peas in mourning? What could have died?" My master was the first to bite on one of the beads and in chewing it broke off a tooth. On Fridays the old harpy usually served us eggs, and so heavily bearded they were with white hairs from her head that they could have been taken for magistrates or men of the law. To use the coal shovel for a soup ladle and bring us broth peppered with cinders was a thing that occurred every day. A thousand times I came across bugs, straws and tow from her spinning wheel in the stew. She put in most anything that might fill us up.

We continued in the same straits up until Lent, at the beginning of which one of our companions took sick. Cabra, to avoid all expense, delayed calling a doctor until the boy was already asking for confession. Finally he called in a cheap quack who on feeling the boy's pulse said that hunger had already beaten him to the punch in killing the youth. The poor lad was given the Blessed Sacraments and when he saw them (he hadn't spoken for a day), he said: "Dear Lord Jesus, I had to see Thee come into this house to convince myself that this place is not hell itself." All this went straight to my heart. The poor boy died, and being a stranger in the community, was buried cheaply. We were all left terror-stricken. The frightful story spread throughout the town and at last reached

Don Alonso's ears. As he had only the one son, he began to recognize what a fraud Cabra was and to give more credence to the complaints of the two shadows of our former selves that both of us had become. He came to the school to take us away and, although we stood right in front of him, he asked where we were. In such a frightful condition did he find us that he waited no longer to tell Master Fasting what a wretch he was and to order us to be carried home in sedan chairs. We took leave of our companions who followed us with their hearts and their eyes, weeping like slaves of the Moors in Algiers watching their fellow prisoners being ransomed by Trinitarian friars.

CHAPTER IV

OUR CONVALESCENCE AND DEPARTURE TO STUDY
AT ALCALA DE HENARES

When we arrived at Don Alonso's house, we were put to bed
very gently so as not to crack our hunger-ridden bones. Our faces
were explored in search of our eyes, but for a long while, because
my work had been heavier and my hunger more intense—after all,
I had been treated like a servant—no one could find mine. Doctors
were called in who ordered our mouths to be dusted out with fox-
tail brushes as though we were veritable paintings of suffering.
They prescribed juices and broths for us. Who would believe how
my stomach lighted up for joy when I drank my first almond milk
and had my first taste of chicken? Everything was a novelty to it.
The doctors ordered that no one speak in a loud voice in our room
for nine whole days because our stomachs were so hollow that every
word set up echoes in them. With these and other precautions, we
began to be ourselves again and to regain our strength, but our jaws
were so lean and pleated they wouldn't limber up. The order was
given to pry them open with the handle of a wood-engraving tool.
After forty days we got out of bed to try our first steps but still we
looked like the shadows of someone else, as thin and yellow as the
seeds of hermits in the wilderness. All day long we thanked the
Almighty for having saved us from that ferocious Old Goat, and
we prayed to the Lord that no Christian ever fall into those cruel
clutches. If ever we happened to think of the meals at the boarding
house while we were eating, the food bills doubled that day. We
often related to Don Alonso how Cabra would sit down at the table
and preach against gluttony, a thing he'd never come in contact with
in all of his life. He laughed heartily when we told him that in the
commandment *Thou shalt not kill,* Cabra included all the partridges,
capons, hens, and the other things he never fed us. Above all, he
applied it to hunger, which, judging from his evasion of eating, it
was a deadly sin either to kill or even to wound.

After three months had gone by like this, Don Alonso began
to plan to send his son Don Diego to Alcalá to finish his education at the university there. He asked me if I would like to go, and
I, who wanted nothing more than to get out of earshot of the name

of that persecutor of the stomach, offered to serve his son in whatever capacity I was able. He appointed a sort of steward to look after him and to keep tab on the boy's expenses which were to be remitted as bills to a man named Julián Merluza. We sent our belongings in the wagon of a fellow named Diego Monje. There was one single bed and two trundle beds, one for me and one for the steward whose name was Tomás de Baranda, five quilts and eight sheets, eight pillows, four carpets, a trunk of linen, and other household furnishings.

We took the coach and left about an hour before dark and arrived just after midnight at the accursed inn of Viveros. The innkeeper was a Moor and a thief in whom the stealth of the cat lived in perfect peace with the dog of an infidel. He received us most graciously since he worked hand in hand with the wagon driver who had arrived with our belongings half an hour earlier because of our slow rate of speed. He even came out to the carriage and offered me his hand to help me alight and asked me if I was going to the university. I replied that I was. I went inside the inn where there were two rough-looking fellows with a couple of girls, a priest saying his prayers, a miserly old merchant cogitating how to avoid buying his supper, and two no-good students busily plotting how to fill their stomachs. My master came in at last and being just a boy, said to the landlord:

"Sir, please prepare whatever you have for me and my servants." "We are all your servants here, sir, (one of the ruffians then said), and ask no more than to serve you. Look here, innkeeper, here's a young gentleman who will be grateful for whatever you do for him. Empty the pantry." After this, one of his pals came up to Don Diego and took his cloak, saying, "Sit down, sir, and relax a bit." I was so puffed up with pride at all this that I felt as though I owned the inn. One of the young nymphs said: "What a good-looking fellow! Is he going to the university? Are you his servant, sir?" I answered, thinking they were all sincere, that the other man and I were his servants. They asked me his name, and no sooner had I told them than one of the students, almost in tears, went up to him, and giving him a tender hug, said: "Oh dear Don Diego! Who would have imagined ten years ago that I would run into you by chance like this? Alas to think I've changed so that you, sir, don't even recognize me!" My master and I were both astonished for we could both have sworn that we'd never laid eyes on the chap in our lives. The other student walked back and forth looking at Don Diego fixedly in the face and finally said to his companion:

"Is this the gentleman whose father you've spoken of so many times? What luck to run into him and to recognize him now that he's grown so. God keep him." And he began to cross himself. Who would have believed that they hadn't grown up with us? Don Diego was very friendly toward him and had just asked his name when the innkeeper came in to set the table, and smelling trickery in the wind, said: "Better do your talking later or the meal will get cold." One of the ruffians put seats around the table for all and an armchair for Don Diego, while the other carried in a platter. The students said: "Go ahead and eat, sir. We'll serve your table while the cook sees what he can find for us."

"Good Lord! (said Don Diego), let's sit down if someone's going to serve us," to which the two young rascals (although they weren't the ones addressed), replied: "In a minute, sir. Everything isn't ready yet." When I saw then how easily invitations were made and how quickly accepted, I began to be a bit afraid. I saw what was going to happen because the students picked up the salad, which was by no means a small one, and looking at my master, said: "It isn't right for these young ladies to go hungry when there's such a fine gentleman present. Won't you ask them, sir, to join us for a bite?" Don Diego made them a gallant invitation. They sat down, and between the two students and the girls, in four quick mouthfuls they finished off all the salad except for a few leaves of lettuce which Don Diego ate. The accursed student passed the bowl to him saying: "One of your grandfathers, sir, my father's uncle, got sick at the sight of lettuce. What an outstanding man he was!" As soon as he had said this, he laid to rest one of the rolls, and the other chap, another. The two whores with them had already written off the loaf of bread, but the glutton of all was the priest, who with his eyes alone devoured more than the others. Our new friends sat down to a side of roast kid, two thick strips of bacon, and a couple of boiled pigeons, and said: "Well, Father, what keeps you over there? Come over and join us. Don Diego is hospitable to all." They no sooner invited him than he came and sat down. My master seeing so many close in on him began to feel worried. They divided everything up and gave Don Diego some bones and some wings. The priest and the others gulped down the rest.

The ruffians said: "Don't eat too much, sir. It might make you ill," to which the accursed student added, "And it's better to eat lightly to prepare yourself for the life at Alcalá." The other servant and I were praying to God they would find it in their hearts to leave us something. After they had already eaten everything and the priest was picking over the bones the others had left, one of the ruffians said: "Bless my soul. We haven't left anything for the servants. Come here please, host. Give them whatever you have." Immediately the long-lost relative of my master (I mean the young scholar), jumped up and said:

"Pardon me for saying so, sir, but apparently you know little about courtesy. Do you perchance know my dear cousin? He will take care of his servants, and would provide for ours as well if we had any and every bit as nicely as he did for us." And turning to Don Diego who was stunned, said: "Don't be angry, sir. After all, they didn't know you before." I really cursed him when I saw such hypocrisy which, I was beginning to think, would never come to an end.

The tables were cleared off and everybody advised Don Diego to go have a good night's sleep. He offered to pay for the supper but they all told him not to as there would be time for that in the morning. While they all were chatting a bit, someone asked the student's name, to which he replied that it was Pedro Coronel. May the scoundrel burn in hell, wherever he may be! He caught sight of the old miser who was sleeping and said: "Do you want to have a good laugh? Let's play a trick on this old boy who's rolling in wealth but is so stingy he wouldn't eat more than an apple on the road." The ruffians said: "The scholar is right. Go ahead. We're with you." With that, he went over to the poor old fellow (who was asleep) and from under his feet slipped some knapsacks. He unfolded them and took out a box. The company gathered round as though it were a prize of war. He opened it up and found it full of candies. These he emptied out and then he put stones, sticks, and whatever he found in their place. He then proceeded to relieve himself over all this, and on the top of all this filth placed about a dozen pieces of plaster. He closed the box and said: "That's not all yet. The old guy still has a wine flask." He poured all the wine out except a little bit at the bottom, and after stuffing the flask with feathers and tow from the cushions of our coach, replaced the cork. After that everybody went off to bed for the remaining hour or so of the night. The student put everything back in the knapsack and placed a large stone in the hood of the man's cloak, and then went off to sleep.

When the time came to start out again, everyone was up except the old man who slept right on. They called him but when he tried to get up, he couldn't raise the hood of his cloak. He looked to see what it was while the innkeeper purposely began to scold him and said: "Good Lord, father, couldn't you find anything else to steal but a stone? What would you gentlemen say to this if I hadn't discovered it? I value it at over a hundred *ducados* as it's a charm against stomach disorders." The old man swore and re-swore that he hadn't put any such stone in his hood.

Our two rough-necks were figuring up the bill, which came to sixty *reales*, a sum the most cunning mathematician of Spain could not have arrived at. The students said: "Just wait till we help you out at Alcalá, sir!" We stood there stunned to see such a bill. We ate a bite of breakfast and the old man got out his knapsack. In order not to risk having to share with us in case we saw the contents, he opened it up in the dark under his cloak. He picked up a well-smeared piece of plaster, stuck it in his mouth, and all but lost the one tooth and stump he had left. He began to spit and make faces like someone in pain. We all ran over to him, the priest in the lead, and asked him what the matter was. He began to call on the devil for help, and dropped the knapsack. The student went up to him and said: "Get thee behind me, Satan. Respect the cross." The priest opened his prayer book and they made the old fool think a devil had possessed him until he told what the trouble was and asked for a little of his wine to rinse out his mouth. They let him do so. He got out and opened the flask and poured a bit of wine into a glass. Out came a ferocious brew full of wool and tow and so clogged with whiskers and fuzz that it could neither be drunk nor strained. The old man really began to lose patience then, but seeing the group convulsed with laughter, he decided to keep quiet and went out to get into the coach with the ruffians and their "lady" friends. The students and the priest mounted their donkeys, and we got into our coach. We had hardly started on our way when the others began to roar with laughter at the tricks played on us. The innkeeper joined in, saying: "Young gentlemen, a few initiations like this one will age you in a hurry." The curate said: "I'm a priest so I'll pay you back in masses." The accursed student yelled: "Scratch when you get a bite, dear cousin, not afterwards." The other called out: "May you get the mange, Don Diego, sir." We tried to pay no attention. The Lord knows how ashamed we felt as we left.

With these and some other incidents we arrived at Alcalá at about nine o'clock. We spent the whole day auditing the bill for the supper of the night before but we were never able to make head or tail of the amount.

CHAPTER V

THE ARRIVAL IN ALCALA, THE INITIATION FEE AND THE TRICKS THAT WERE PLAYED ON ME AS A NEWCOMER

Before nightfall we left the inn to go to the house that had been rented for us. It was right outside the Gate of Santiago, a sort of square where many students lived, though in our section there were only three other residents. The owner and landlord of the place was one of those who believe in God for the sake of appearance or through sham. The people call them Moriscos and they abound hereabouts as well as those with long noses. They can smell out anything but pork. I say this, but I confess there is certainly a large number of fine people among the upper classes. The landlord, then, received me with a sterner look than if I had been the Holy Sacrament. I don't know if he received us like that to instill in us a certain amount of respect or if that was his way. After all it isn't surprising that a man of bad religious principles should have a bad character. We brought in our belongings, set up the beds, arranged the other things and slept there that night. Early the next morning all of the students of the section came in their nightshirts to ask my master for the customary initiation fee. He, not knowing the custom, asked what they meant. Meanwhile, afraid of what might happen, I hid myself under the covers and left only the top of my head sticking out, like a turtle's. They asked for two dozen *reales*. Don Diego gave it to them and then they all began yelling like demons and shouted: "Hurrah for our comrade. He's one of us. Give him all the privileges of an upperclassman. May he get the itch and be as dirty and hungry as the rest of us!" And with that —what privileges!—they flew down the stairs; just as quickly we both got dressed.

We started to school. Several students who knew my master's father adopted him and took him off to the classroom, but I who had to go in another direction and who was alone began to tremble. I went out into the square and hardly placed a foot into it when I came face to face with a group of students. They began to shout, "A new one!" To conceal my fear, I laughed as though I didn't care what they said, but it wasn't enough, for eight or nine of them

45

came up to me and began to laugh at me. I blushed; would to God I hadn't because immediately one of the fellows right beside me put his hand up to his nose and moved away and said: "This Lazarus must be ready for raising from the dead judging by the way he smells." With that they all moved away, all holding their noses. Hoping to get away, I held my nose too and said: "You're quite right, gentlemen, something does smell around here." They burst out laughing; about a hundred of them had gathered. They began to swagger about and to sound the call to arms; in their coughing and the opening and closing of their mouths I saw that they were working up a lot of phlegm. Then a big fellow with a bad cold shot a terrible mouthful at me. Seeing I was lost I started to say: "I swear to God that I'll . . ."; and was going to say "kill you," but the batteries opened up and the rain of snot that fell on me made me lose my wits. I could see that some of the blobs they had coughed up were long enough to be their owner's intestines. Some of my attackers ran out of saliva and had to fall back on what they found in their noses. They came up with shot made of dried bits of snot that was so hard that it left my cape all battered and dented. I had covered my face with my cloak which was white from their spitting. You should have seen how good their aim was. I was snow-white from head to foot, but one dirty wretch, seeing how I had protected my face, came up to me and said angrily: "That's enough. You don't want to kill him." I who, judging from the treatment they were giving me, thought they would kill me, uncovered my face to see who it was. At the same time the fellow who had shouted out had worked up a mouthful of greenish mucus which he let fly and nailed me right between the eyes. You can imagine how miserable I was. That crowd of devils let out such a shout that it made me dizzy, and I, to judge from the way they had emptied their stomachs all over me, decided they must use new students as a form of purge to save going to the doctor or druggist. Besides all this, they wanted to beat me, but they couldn't find a spot to hit without getting their hands in the cosmetics of my black cloak, now as white as innocence. So they let me off, and I started towards home, which I could hardly find. Luckily, it being morning, I only encountered two or three boys who must have been well inclined towards me because they only threw four or five dirty rags at me and then let me go on my way. I entered the house where the Moslem landlord saw me, began to laugh and act as if he were going to spit on me too. I feared he would and so I said: "Wait a minute, sir. I'm no *Ecce-Homo*." I should never have said it for he gave me two good blows on the back with

46

some weights he was holding. With the aid of this expensive remark and half crippled, I went upstairs where I passed quite a while searching for a spot to take hold of my cloak so I could take it off. I finally succeeded and hung it out on the roof; then I threw myself down on the bed. My master came in, and finding me asleep and not knowing about my loathsome adventure, got very angry and began to pull my hair so that with a couple more tugs I would have wakened up bald. I jumped up shouting and complaining while he, even angrier, yelled: "Is this the way to work, Pablos? You're already in Paradise." When I heard him say "Paradise," I thought that I must be dead and said: "A lot of comfort you are in my trials, sir. Look at that cloak that's served as handkerchief to noses as big as any ever seen during Holy Week processions. Just look at my ribs." And with that I began to cry. Seeing how upset I was he believed me, and looking at the cloak began to console me by saying: "Pablos, keep your eyes open or your goose will be cooked. You must look out for yourself because here you have no mother and father to do it for you." I told him all that had happened. He told me to get undressed and to go to my room where four other servants of students slept.

I got to bed and slept until evening when, after a good supper, I felt as strong as if nothing had happened to me. But when troubles start, it seems they never end, but come chained link to link, and one leads to another. The other servants came in to bed and greeted me, asking me if I were ill and how I happened to be in bed. I told them my story and right away they began to bless themselves and say innocently: "Such a thing wouldn't even happen among Lutherans. Who ever heard of such a thing!" Another said: "The dean's to blame for not being strict enough. Sir, could you identify the ones who did it?" I answered that I couldn't and thanked them for the interest they had shown in me. After that they all undressed, got in bed, put out the light and off to sleep I went feeling as though I were right at home with my father and brothers.

It must have been midnight when one of them woke me by shouting: "They're killing me! Thieves!" Through the shouting, the sound of whipping came from his bed. I raised my head and said: "What's going on?" and had hardly got the words out of my mouth when on my back landed a lash from a cat-o'-nine-tails. I began to yell and tried to get up. The other fellow was yelling too, but the blows were falling only on me. I began to shout: "In God's name, justice!" But the blows fell so thickly on me that nothing was left for me to do—the covers had been pulled off me—but to get under the bed. I did so and right away the three who were sleeping began

to cry out too, and as the blows still rang out I supposed that someone outside the group was giving us all a beating. Meanwhile, the
devil who slept next to me came over to my bed and relieved himself in it and pulled up the covers over the mess. When he got back
to his own bed again the blows ceased, and all four got up shouting at the top of their lungs: "That's a vile trick nobody should
get away with." I was still under my bed, whimpering like a puppy
locked outside in the cold and so doubled up I looked like a greyhound having a cramp. The others acted as if they were closing the
door. Meanwhile I crept out of my hiding place and climbed into
bed, asking the others if they were hurt. They all complained they
were half dead.

I lay down, covered myself, and soon fell asleep; and as in
my dreams I wallowed about in the bed, I awoke to find myself
covered with filth to the very hair of my head. The others all got
up, but I used the beating as a pretext for not getting dressed.
Devils couldn't have moved me from one side. I was confused,
wondering if perhaps as a consequence of my fright and embarrassment I had done so disgusting a thing in my dreams without
realizing it. I felt innocent and guilty at one and the same time
without knowing how to vindicate myself. My companions came
over to me, grumbling and feigning concern, to ask me how I was.
I replied that I felt terrible because of the severe beating I had
received. I asked them who could have done it, to which they answered: "We swear he'll never get away with it. We know an
astrologer who will tell us who did it. But forgetting that for a
moment, let's see where you're hurt, you're complaining so much."
With that they tried to pull off the covers in order to shame me.
Just then my master came in saying: "Can't I do anything with
you, Pablos? It's eight o'clock and you're still in bed? Get up
right away." The others, to help me, told Don Diego the whole
story and asked him to let me sleep. One of them said: "If you
don't believe us, sir, have our friend show you." Then he grabbed
the covers. I had them clenched in my teeth so as to keep the turds
covered up. When they saw that they couldn't uncover me that way,
one said: "My Lord but it stinks in here!" Don Diego said the
same, for it was true. Then, following him, they all began to look
around the room to see if someone had left a chamber pot. They
decided it couldn't be that. One said: "Well, this is a good subject
for us to study." They examined the beds and moved them to see
underneath. Finally they said: "No doubt there is something under
Pablos' bed. Let's lift him to another one and look under it." Seeing
there was no remedy to the business and that I was wholly in their

clutches, I pretended that I was having a heart attack and grabbed the sides of the bed, grimacing with pain. Since they already had the key to the mystery, they held me still and said: "What a shame!" Don Diego took me by the middle finger and finally between the five of them, they lifted me. On raising the sheets they all laughed so hard at the sight of my nest of pigeons, little and big, that they almost brought down the house. "Poor chap," said the deceitful devils; I pretended to be in a dead faint. "Pull hard on that finger, sir," and my master, thinking he was being helpful, pulled so hard that he got it out of joint. The others then wanted to put a tourniquet on my thigh and said: "The poor fellow must have filthied himself when the attack started." No one can imagine what I felt inside, with such shame, a finger disjointed, and the danger I ran from their tourniquet. At last from fear of this latter—the cords were already biting into my thigh—I acted as though I had just come to. Even that fast, the devils had been so intent on their task that the cords had already sunk two fingers deep into each leg. They stopped, and said to me: "Lord, how thin you are." I was so angry I cried, and they said pointedly: "Your health, my friend, is more important than keeping clean, so keep quiet." And with that they washed me, put me back to bed, and left.

I came to the conclusion that what had happened to me in one day at Alcalá was worse than anything at Cabra's. At noon, I got dressed, cleaned my cloak as thoroughly as possible—washing it with an old rag—, and waited for my master who asked me, when he arrived, how I was. All the fellows of the house went to eat and I joined them, although I had no appetite and had little to eat. Afterwards when we got together to chat in the corridor, the other servants, after kidding me a bit, confessed the whole prank. They all laughed heartily which doubled my annoyance, and so I resolved to myself: "On guard, Pablos. Be alert." I determined to lead a new life. With that, we all became friends and from then on all of us in the house lived together like brothers, and neither in class nor on the campus did anyone trouble me again.

CHAPTER VI

CONCERNING THE HARD-HEARTED THINGS THE
HOUSEKEEPER DID, AND PRANKS I PLAYED

"When in Rome, do as the Romans do," says the adage, and rightly so. I took heed of the lesson and resolved to become a rogue among rogues and to better them if possible. I don't know how well I succeeded but I assure you, sir, I did everything I could to do so. First of all I passed a death sentence on all the pigs that wandered into the house, and on all the housekeeper's chickens who strayed from their coop into my room. It happened that one day two of the noblest hogs I ever saw in my life wandered in. I was playing a game with the other servants when I heard them grunt and said to one of my friends: "Go see who's grunting in our house." He went, and said that it was two hogs. When I heard this I got so angry that I went out saying that it was a pretty piece of villainy and daring to come grunting into other people's homes. After that I ran both of them through with a sword—after closing the door— and then finished them off by slitting their throats. So that nobody would hear the noise they made, we all began singing as loud as we could and thus the pigs expired at our hands. We took out their innards, saved the blood, and with a fire of straw from our beds, singed them out in the yard. That way when our masters arrived it was all finished, although badly, for we hadn't yet made the blood pudding and, not for lack of haste but because of so much to do, we had left the guts with half their natural contents. Don Diego and our steward found out the whole affair and became so angry with me that the other lodgers—they were laughing so they were useless—had to take my part. Don Diego asked me what I could say for myself if I were accused and arrested. I replied that I would give my reason as hunger, which is sacred to all students. If that wouldn't suffice I would say: "Since they came through the door as if they owned the house, I just supposed they belonged to us." Everybody laughed at my defense. Don Diego said: "One thing is sure, Pablos, you know your weapons." It was indeed extraordinary to see my master so serious and religious and me such a devil, so much so that the virtue of one made the vices of the other stand out even more.

The housekeeper was bursting with joy to have found herself a partner; we had joined forces for raids on the larder. I became a Judas of a steward who ever since has had a sort of inclination towards the thieving such a profession engenders. Meat in the housekeeper's hands never kept the usual mathematical progression, for it always went from more to less. When she could obtain ewe or goat she never served mutton; and if there were bones, no meat got to the table. She made stews that were consumptive from lack of flesh and broths so clear that if solidified they could have been used for making crystal beads. On Easter, to give us a change and to make the soup thicker, she would throw in a couple of tallow candles. When I was with my master, she would say: "There's no one as good a servant as our little Pablos, except for his devilishness. But keep him with you, sir, for it's easy enough to put up with prankishness in return for loyalty. He brings the best the market has to offer." In return, I would say the same about her. Together we deceived the whole household. Sometimes we bought things in quantity and then we would hide half the coal and bacon. When we noticed the loss we would say: "Gentlemen, you'll have to cut down expenses for truly, if you go on at such a rate, a king's ransom will not suffice. Already half the oil and coal are gone, but it's been used up at a pretty fast pace. You'd better order more, gentlemen, and to be sure, it'll have to be used in a different manner. Give the money to Pablos." The money was given to me and we stole the stolen half; and from what we bought new, half was stolen again. That's the way we did with everything. If once in a while I bought something in the square at the correct price, the housekeeper and I would purposely start an argument. She would say angrily: "Don't tell me, Pablos, that this is two *cuartos* worth of lettuce." I would pretend I was crying and argue lustily. Then I would go off to explain to my master and persuade him to send the steward to check on me so that the housekeeper, who purposely kept on arguing, would quiet down. He went and found out; and with that we gave proof to the master and the steward, both of us earning their thanks, I for my honesty and the housekeeper for her care for their welfare. Very satisfied with my performance, Don Diego would say to her: "I just wish Pablos were half as virtuous as he is loyal."

In this manner we were able to suck them like leeches. I'll bet, sir, you'd be amazed at the sum of money we accumulated

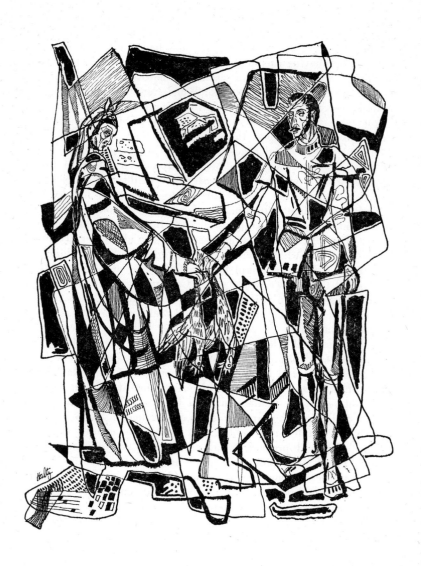

in a year's time. It must have been a lot, but we never had to return any of it, for the housekeeper went to confession and took communion every week. Never did I see the trace of a disposition to return anything, nor of scruples, even though, as I say, she was so saintly. Around her neck she always wore a rosary so large that it would have been less burdensome to carry a bundle of firewood over her shoulders. From it hung handfuls of holy medals, crosses and indulgences. On all of them she said she prayed nightly for her benefactors. She counted a hundred and some saints who were her patrons, and truly she had need of all their help to compensate for all her sins. She slept in a room above my master's and said more prayers than a blind beggar. She began with the prayer called the "Just Judge" and finished with the *Cunquibult* and the *Salve Regina*. She recited her prayers in Latin so as to appear more innocent, while we all would split our sides with laughter. She had other talents. She was an acquirer of pleasure and an arranger of desires, which is to say she was a madam. She made the excuse to me that she came by her abilities through heredity, like the monarchs of France with their gift of curing scrofula.

You will suppose, sir, that we always lived in peace, but who does not know that two friends, when they're greedy and, if they are together, will sooner or later try to trick each other? It so happened that the housekeeper raised hens in the yard. I had a desire to eat one of them. She had twelve or thirteen well-fed chickens, and one day while she was feeding them, she began to call them by saying: "Pío, pío." When I heard her use this expression, I began to shout at her: Oh, God save us, housekeeper. If you had murdered a man or stolen money from the King's treasury I could have kept quiet, but since you have done what you did, it's impossible not to report it. The Lord have mercy on both of us!" She, seeing me so deeply upset, became disturbed herself and said: "Why, Pablos, what have I done? If you're trying to kid me, don't overwork yourself." "What do you mean, kid you? I wish I were! I can't avoid my duty to inform the Inquisition because if I don't I'll be excommunicated." "Inquisition? she said and began to tremble. "What could I have done against the faith?" "That's the worst of it," I replied. "Don't try to joke with the Inquisitors. Say you were an idiot and that you retract but don't deny your blasphemy and irreverence." Full of fright, she said, "But, Pablos, if I recant, will they punish me?" I answered: "No, because they will give you absolution." "Then I recant," she said, "but tell me what I did. Surely I didn't know, as the souls of my dead loved ones will bear me out." "Is it possible you didn't realize what you did? I don't know how to tell you, for the irreverence is so great it frightens me. Don't you remember how you called the chickens with "pío, pío," time and again, and that Pius is the name of popes, the vicars of God and heads of the Church? What sin for the pious!" She stood there like someone who had been struck dead and said: "Pablos, I admit it, but may the Lord not forgive me if I did it intentionally. I retract it. Think of some way so you won't have to accuse me, for if I have to go before the Inquisition I'll die first." "If you swear on a holy altar that it was unintentional, I'll be reassured enough to avoid informing against you. But you will have to give me those two chickens who were eating while you were calling them by the most holy name of the Pontiffs so that I can take them to an officer who can burn them, for they're surely damned. Besides that, you'll have to swear never to backslide." Feeling very satisfied, she said: "Why, take them with you now, Pablos. Tomorrow I'll swear to it." To drive this all home, I went on: "The worst of it is, Cipriana—that was her name—that I run the risk, because the Inquisitor will accuse me of being the guilty one and could cause me a lot of trouble. You take them yourself because, by God, I'm afraid." "Pablos," she said when she heard this, "in the name of God, have pity on me and take them. Nothing can happen to you."

I let her plead with me for a while and finally I decided to do it, took the chickens, hid them in my room, and acted as though I were going out. Then I came back in saying: "It turned out better than I thought it would. The Inquisitor wanted to follow me to see who the woman was, but I did a pretty piece of work fooling and handling him."

She kept hugging me and gave me another chicken for myself. Off I went with it to my room. I had a baker make a pie which I shared with the other servants. The housekeeper and Don Diego found out the whole affair and the whole household was highly entertained by it all. The housekeeper came in so terribly upset that she was ready to die. From sheer anger she was on the verge—not having any more reason to keep silent—of exposing all my thievery.

Seeing I was in bad with the old woman and couldn't play any more tricks on her, I began to search out new plans to amuse myself. I decided on what the students call snatching and shoplifting. These gave me many pleasant adventures, because one night at nine o'clock —when few people were about—as I was going down the main street, I spied a confectioner's shop inside of which was a tray of raisins on the counter. I snatched it up and began to run away. The confectioner started after me and a crowd of servants and neighbors followed suit. Overburdened as I was I saw that although I had a head start, they were going to overtake me. Therefore, on turning a corner, I sat down on the tray. Then I quickly put a cape around my legs and holding one of them, began to yell: "God forgive him, he stepped right on me." They heard this, and when they got close, I began to say: "In the name of the Holy Virgin," and the usual stuff about "the hour of evil" and "the poisonous air." They arrived shouting at the top of their voices and asked me: "Did a man go by here, brother?" "Straight ahead," I answered. "He stepped on me right here, praise the Lord."

With that they started on again and disappeared. I was left alone to carry my tray home and tell the story which everyone applauded a great deal, but which no one would believe had really happened. So to show them, I invited them to watch me swipe a box of sweets another night.

They came along, but when they saw the boxes well out of arm's reach inside the shop, they decided it was an impossible feat, especially since the confectioner—because of what had happened to the raisins—was very much on his guard. I got there; then, some dozen paces from the shop, having drawn my sword, which was a stout one, I broke into a run and as I arrived at the shop, yelled: "Drop dead!" I made a thrust right in front of the confectioner. He fell to his kness begging for a confessor. I continued my thrust on through the box of sweets, drawing it out on my sword, then running away with it. They were all astonished at the feat, and half dead with laughing at the confectioner for asking that someone look to him. He thought sure he had been wounded by a man with whom he had had a dispute. But as he rolled his eyes up and saw the boxes in a heap because of the one I had pulled out, he caught on to the hoax and began to bless himself as though he'd never get through. I confess that I never pulled a better stunt in my life. My companions asserted that I could support the whole household with what I "lifted" alone, which is the crook's way of saying "to steal."

As I was only a boy and saw how they all praised the ingenuity with which I carried out these escapades, I was encouraged to do more of them. Every day I brought my waistband full of nuns' drinking vessels which I got by asking for a drink and then running off with the cup. Finally, because of my thieving, they refused to hand anything out without first having something for security. Thus it happened that I promised Don Diego and all his friends that one night I would disarm the watch. We decided on the night it was to be, and all set out with me at the head. Discerning the watch at a distance, I ran up to them with another of the servants from the house, both of us very excited, and said: "Police?" They answered: "Yes." "Is the chief with you?" They said that he was. I knelt down and said: "Sir, in your Honor's hands is the power to right a wrong and to revenge evil and to do the public a great service. I beg your Honor to listen to a couple of words in private if you want to make an important arrest." He stepped aside, and already the cops were grasping their swords and others their clubs. I continued: "Sir, I have come from Seville in pursuit of six of the most villainous men in the world, all thieves and murderers. One of them killed my mother and one of my brothers while robbing them, and it's definitely proven against him. From what I've heard, they're accompanied by a French spy, and I even suspect, from their conversation, that he was sent—here I lowered my voice to a whisper— by the King's ex-favorite and worst enemy, Antonio Pérez."

With that the chief leaped up and shouted: "Where are they?" "Sir, in a bawdyhouse. Don't hesitate, sir," I said, "for the souls of my mother and brother will repay you with their prayers, and the King reward you." "My God!" he said, "Let's not lose time. All of you follow me, and hand me a buckler." Taking him aside again, I said: "Sir, your Honor will only spoil it all if you do that. The only way to do it is for all of you to go in without swords, one by one, for they are all in the girls' rooms and have pistols with them. As soon as they saw you with swords, which only the watch can carry, they would fire. It's better to use daggers and get them from behind, for there are enough of us."

The chief, greedy for the arrest, approved my plan. When we got fairly close, the chief, acting on my advice, ordered the men to hide their swords in the grass of a field in front of the house. They hid them and moved on. I had already told the other servant to pick up the swords and make off for the house with them as soon as they put them down. He followed instructions. When they went in, I stayed well behind, and once they had mixed in with some other people who had gone in with them, I took to my heels down the street that comes out near La Victoria, running so fast that a greyhound couldn't have caught me. Once they were inside and saw that there were only students and blackguards, which is all the same, they began to look for me. Not finding me, they suspected what had happened. They went to get their swords but there wasn't a sign of them. Who could have imagined what a thorough search the dean and the chief would make that night? They went from building to building, checking every face and looking at every weapon. They got to our house. So that they wouldn't recognize me, I was stretched out in bed with a nightcap on, a candle in one hand and a crucifix in the other, with one of the Divinity students helping me to die while the others chanted the Litany. The dean came in with the police; when they saw such a spectacle they went out again, persuaded that no one there could have played such a prank. Discovering nothing, the dean said a prayer for the dying. He asked if I was already speechless and was told that I was. With that they all left, having given up all hope of finding a trace. The dean swore to give up the culprit if he found him, and the police chief to hang him even though he were the son of the most powerful noble in the land. I got out of bed, and to this day they haven't stopped laughing over this prank at Alcalá.

To avoid being tedious I'll not tell how I turned the market square into a forestry preserve. With crates from tailors and silversmiths, and tables from the fruit stalls—for I never forgot the insult I suffered as "King of the Roost"—I supplied our fireplace throughout the year. I won't mention the pension I exacted from the bean fields, vineyards, and orchards of the countryside round about. With these and other things I began to become famous for being both mischievous and witty. The young gentlemen showed me so much attention that I hardly had time to serve Don Diego, to whom, however, I always showed the proper respect because of the affection he had always had for me.

Chapter VII

CONCERNING THE DEPARTURE OF DON DIEGO, THE NEWS OF THE DEATH OF MY PARENTS AND THE RESOLUTION I MADE ABOUT MY FUTURE

About this time, Don Diego received a letter from his father in which was enclosed another from an uncle of mine named Alonso Ramplón, a man well known in Segovia for his devotion to justice, for in the last forty years so much of it had been carried out by his very own hand. To tell the truth, he was the hangman, and as watchful as an eagle in the execution of his profession. To see him at work inspired one to want to be hanged. This was the man, then, who wrote me at Alcalá from Segovia, as follows:

LETTER

"Son Pablos (because of the great love he bore me he addressed me that way): The weighty affairs of the position in which His Majesty has placed me have left me no time to write sooner; for if the service of the King has any fault, it is work, although this is compensated for by the honor we have of being his servants. It grieves me to give you news that is hardly pleasant. Your father died a week ago with as great a courage as any man has ever died. I speak from knowledge, as it was I who hanged him. He mounted the ass without touching a foot to the stirrups; the prison clothes fit him so well that they could have been tailored for him and since he made so fine an appearance, no one seeing him with the crucifixes before him would have thought he was about to be hanged. He went along quite relaxed looking at the windows and bowing to those who left their work to look out at him. Twice he twirled his moustache; he even told the priests who were to administer last rites to be at their ease and praised them for their good work. Once at the foot of the gallows, he climbed the ladder neither on all fours nor slowly, and seeing one of the rungs broken, he turned to the officials and told them to have it repaired for the next man, since not everyone had his bravery. I could scarcely overrate the good impression he made on everybody. He sat down at the top and straightened out the wrinkles in his clothes. Then he took the rope and put it around his neck, and seeing that the monk wanted to give a sermon, he turned to him and said, "Father, I consider the sermon preached. Give us a bit of the Creed and let's finish up in a hurry for I wouldn't want this to get tedious." That's how it was done. He entreated me to put his hood to one side and wipe off his beard, and I did it for him. He swung without doubling up his legs or doing any twitching. Instead he hung there with so serious a look to him that nothing more desirable for the occasion could have been asked. I quartered him and made the highway his tomb. God knows what grief it causes me to see him out there making a free meal for the crows, but I understand that the pastry cooks of hereabouts will put our minds at ease by using him up in four-penny meat pies. As for your mother, although she is alive right now, I can almost say the same for her, as she is a prisoner of the Inquisition of Toledo because she disinterred the dead without informing a soul. It was said that every night, using that eye that hasn't a twin, she gave satisfaction to a he-goat. In her house were found more legs, arms, and heads than in a chapel where miracles are performed, and the least of her feats was the restoration of maidenheads and the falsification of virgins. They say that she will appear in an auto-da-fe on Trinity Sunday with four hundred others destined to die. It's very upsetting to me as it is a disgrace to us all and mostly to me who am, after all, a representative of the King and for whom such family connections are damaging. Son, some sort of belongings have been left here which your parents had managed to hide away. In all, it should mount up to about four hundred *ducados;* I'm your uncle, so whatever I have is yours. In view of this, you can come here and with your knowledge of Latin and rhetoric you'll make a singular success of the art of execution. Answer me soon, and meanwhile, may God watch over you."

I can't deny that I was very upset by this new disgrace, but there was a partial satisfaction in it; so may the vices of parents, however great, bring comfort to their children in time of misfortune. I ran off to find Don Diego. He was reading the letter from his father in which he was told to come home but not to bring me with him since he was upset to hear of my pranks. He told me that he had decided to go, and what his father had ordered him to do, and that he was grieved at the thought of leaving me. He told me that

59

he would arrange a position for me with a young gentleman friend of his whom I could serve. Hearing this, I said laughingly, "Sir, I have changed, and so has my thinking, I am aiming at a higher and more authoritative post. If up to the present, like just anybody else, I had only my foot on a rung of the ladder, I now have my father's example." I related to him how he had died with as much honor as the most avaricious; how they cut him up into quarters and how my uncle the executioner had written me all this, and about the imprisonment of my mother. To Don Diego, who knew my background, I could tell everything without any shame. He was very sorry for me and asked me what I thought I would do. I told him what I had decided on, and with that he left for Segovia the next day, very sad, while I stayed in the house and pretended I was untouched by my misfortune. I burned the letter for fear that if I were to lose it, someone else might read it. I began to arrange for my departure for Segovia with the intention of claiming my inheritance and meeting my relatives, so later on I could keep away from them.

CHAPTER VIII

CONCERNING THE JOURNEY FROM ALCALA TO SEGOVIA
AND WHAT HAPPENED ON THE WAY AS FAR AS
REJAS, WHERE I STOPPED TO PASS THE NIGHT

The day came to leave behind the best life I had ever known.
The good Lord knows what I felt on leaving so many acquaintances
and good friends without number. I sold what few belongings I had,
for money for the trip, and with the help of a few tricks, made almost six hundred *reales*. I hired a mule and left the lodgings from
which I had nothing more to take than my shadow. Who could depict
the suffering of the shoemaker over his bill, the clamor of the
housekeeper for her pay, and the shouts of the landlord of the house
for his rent? One of them said, "I always knew it in my heart."
Another, "They certainly told me that fellow was a swindler." In
other words, I departed from town so well loved by the people that
I left half of them in tears over my absence, and the other half
laughing at those who were crying.

I went along my way amusing myself by thinking about these
things when, passing Torote, I met a man on a pack-mule. He was
talking to himself at a great rate and so absorbed in himself that
he didn't even see me. I greeted him and he greeted me. I asked
him where he was heading and after we had exchanged answers, we
began to discuss whether the power of the Turks was weakening
and what was happening to the forces of the King. He began to
propound a scheme for the conquest of the Holy Land and how we
could take Algiers. From this I could easily see that he was crazy on
the subject of politics and government. We continued this conversation, best fit for scoundrels, and finally got around, after one thing
and another, to talking about the troubles in Flanders. Here he
began to sigh and said: "Those countries have cost me more than
they have the King. For fourteen years now I have been working
on a project, which if it weren't impracticable, as it happens to be,
would be arranged by now."

"What sort of thing can that be," I said, "that while it's so
advantageous, is impracticable and cannot be carried out?"

61

"Who told you, sir," he continued, "that it cannot be carried out? It can be done. To be impracticable is something else. If it weren't for fear of annoying you I would explain to you, sir, what it is; but it will all be brought to light, as at the moment I expect to have it published with some other short works, among which I suggest to the King how to take Ostend by two different ways."

I begged him to tell me about them, so, after taking some papers out of his pockets, he showed me a sketch of both the enemy stronghold and our own. Then he said: "You can see very well, sir, that the difficulty of the situation lies in this inlet of the sea. Well, I would give the order to suck it all up with sponges and so remove the obstacle."

On hearing such nonsense I burst out laughing, while he, looking me straight in the face, said:

"Everybody that I have told about the plan reacted to it just as you did. They are all delighted with it."

"I'm quite sure they are," I replied, "to hear so novel and so sound an idea. But you will have to take into account that once you have soaked up the water that was there before, the sea will turn right around to put more in its place."

"The sea will do no such thing for I have already planned for that," he answered me. "I have worked out an invention to lower the sea thereabouts twelve fathoms."

I didn't dare reply to this for fear he might have the means to bring the sky down on top of us. Never in my life have I seen such a lunatic. He said that the great Juanelo [who had brought the water supply to the highest sections of Toledo] had done nothing; that he himself was laying out plans to bring the whole Tajo River into Toledo, which was much more practical. Explaining how he would do it, he said he would do it by casting a spell. Well, sir, whoever heard of such a thing! Finally, he said to me. "I don't intend to put it into execution unless, first, the King presents me with an estate, which I could manage very well for I have quite honorable ancestry." With such confused conversation, we arrived at Torrejón where he stopped off to see a relative of his.

I went on ahead half dead with laughter at the projects with which he filled his time, when, the Lord and luck being on my side, I saw a mule in the distance. By its side there was a man who, as he looked at a book, was drawing out some lines which he measured with a compass. He was leaping and jumping from one side to the other, and from time to time would cross his fingers and make numerous strange movements. I must admit that for quite a while — for I had stopped at some distance away to watch him — I believed him to be a magician and had almost decided not to go on. When I got near to him, he noticed me and closed the book. Then as he put one foot in the stirrup, he slipped and fell down. He picked himself up and said to me, "I didn't take the measurement of the proportion well enough to determine the circumference to mount." I didn't understand what he had said to me, but soon my fears were answered, for he was the craziest man that was ever born of womankind. He asked me if I was going to Madrid by straight line or if I was taking a circumflex route. Although I didn't understand him at all, I replied that I was taking the circumflex. He asked me whose sword I was wearing at my side, which, I answered, was mine. "Those cross-guards should be longer to make up for the cutting stroke formed over the center of the thrust." Then he began such a preposterous discourse that I felt obliged to ask him what trade he professed. He answered me that he was a true swordsman and that he would back up his claims wherever he might be. I was bursting out laughing and said to him: "To tell you the truth, sir, from what I saw you doing in the fields I took you for a magician, seeing the circles you were making." "That," he said, "was because I had an idea for a quarter-circular thrust with the major compass lengthening the sword movement and thereby killing the opponent before he could even confess or know who had done it. Furthermore I was just reducing it to mathematical terms."

"Can it be," I said to him, "that mathematics enter into this?"

He replied, "Not only mathematics, but theology, philosophy, music and medicine."

"Of the last I have no doubt since the aim of the art is killing."

"Don't laugh," he went on, "for I am just learning to use a new guard, the brusher, by making the finest of thrusts which contain in themselves the spirals of the sword."

"I don't understand a thing you are telling me, large or small."

"Why," he went on, "it's all explained here in this book, which is called *The Marvels of the Sword*. It's a fine book which tells marvelous things. So that you will believe this, in Rejas, where we will spend the night, you will see me perform wonders with a couple of spits. Have no doubts that anyone who reads this book will be able to kill anyone he may like to. The man who wrote it was a very learned man, and I could put it even stronger than that."

We were still chatting when we arrived in Rejas. We came to an inn, and on alighting he called out to me in a loud voice to make an obtuse angle of my legs and then to reduce them to parallel lines to deposit myself perpendicularly on the ground. The landlord saw me laugh and began to laugh himself. He asked me if the gentleman was an Indian for he talked like one. Between the two of them I thought I would lose my mind. Finally my companion went up to the landlord and said, "Sir, let me have a couple of spits for two or three angles; I'll return them right away."

"Sweet Jesus!" exclaimed the landlord, "give the angles to me so my wife can roast them, though they're birds whose name I never heard before."

"They are not birds," he said turning towards me. "Just see, sir, what it means to be ignorant. Give me the spits for I only want them for a bit of swordsmanship. What you see me do today may be of more value to you than all that you have learned in your whole lifetime."

As it happened the spits were being used so we had to take two large spoons. Never in the world was a funnier sight to be seen. He made a leap and said: "With this motion I reach more, and I reach the degrees of the profile. Now I take advantage of the remiss movement to do away with the natural one. This one should be a thrust, and this one a cut." He didn't come within a mile of me and was dancing about with his spoon. Since I just stood still, it looked as if his feints would have to be scoops and the target a stew standing on the fire. He said to me: "This is, after all, the true art, and not the drunken foolishness taught by those villainous fencing masters who know only how to drink."

He had hardly finished saying this when from another room there stepped a mulatto whose teeth shone like tusks. He wore a hat the size of an umbrella, and a jacket underneath a loose-fitting cloak all covered with ribbons. He was as knock-kneed as an imperial eagle. On his cheek he carried evidence of his enemies' blessing: a sign of the cross was carved there. Above a bristling beard were two moustaches the size of hand guards on a sword, while hanging at his side was a dagger with more metal work on it than on a nun's grating. Looking down at the floor, this fellow said: "I have been examined and have my diploma, and by the sun that warms the wheat fields, I'll cut to pieces anyone who speaks ill of the brave boys who profess that skill." Understanding the situation, I stepped between the two and said that since my comrade was not speaking to him, he had no reason to get angry. "Draw your sword," he said, "if you have one, and let's settle which one is the real swordsman here. Forget this child's play with spoon handles." My poor friend opened his book and replied in a loud voice: "This book explains all, and since it's printed under the authority of the King, I uphold that what it states is true, with a spoon or without a spoon, either here or anywhere else, and if not, let's take measure-

ments." He took out his compass and said: "This angle is obtuse."
Just as quickly, the fencing master drew his dagger and said: "I
don't know who Angle is, nor Obtuse, nor did I ever hear such names
before in my life. But with this hand, I'll carve you to pieces." He
ran at the poor devil and began to slash at him. My friend began
to leap about the house crying, "He can't wound me for I have won
on degrees of the profile." The landlord and I and the rest of the
audience made peace between them, though we were laughing so
hard we could hardly move.

The good old man was taken up to his room, and me with him.
We ate and everybody went to bed. At two o'clock in the morning,
he got up in his nightshirt and began to walk around the room in
the dark, hopping about and chattering nonsense in mathematic
terminology. He woke me, and not content with that, went down to
ask a light of the landlord saying that he had discovered a fixed
object on the sagitta thrust of the bow. The landlord told him to
go to the devil for waking him up and was so furious that he called
him a lunatic. With that he came back up and told me that if I
would get up, he would show me the famous thrust he had invented
for use against the Turks and their scimitars; he explained that
he wanted to go immediately to demonstrate it to the King because of the advantages it would bring to the Catholics. By this time,
the sun was up and we all dressed and paid our bill. We made peace
between my friend and the fencing master, who left saying that
my companion's theories were good, but that they made more lunatics
than skilled swordsmen because most people, at least, did not understand them.

CHAPTER IX

CONCERNING WHAT HAPPENED TO ME ON THE
WAY TO MADRID WITH A POET

I set out on the road to Madrid. My friend said farewell as
he was going in another direction. After he had already gone off a
way, he turned back hurriedly and began to call me. When he got
to me, even though we were in the open country where no one could
hear us, he whispered in my ear: "On your life, sir, say nothing
about all those deep secrets that I confided to you regarding swordsmanship. Keep them to yourself as a person of discreet judgment."
I promised him to do so. He left me again, and I began to laugh
at such a humorous secret.

With that, I walked more than a league without meeting anyone. I went along thinking to myself of the many difficulties there
were in professing honor and virtue. First it was necessary for me
to collect the small inheritance from my parents and then, once I got
it, to get out of earshot of any knowledge of them. These seemed to
me to be such honorable thoughts that I complimented myself on
them. I said to myself: "I have much to be proud of, for I had no
one from whom to learn virtue while others merely inherit it from
their forefathers."

With these thoughts and monologues in my head, I was walking
along when I met a very ancient clergyman on muleback, also going
to Madrid. We fell to chatting and he asked me where I came from.
I told him, from Alcalá. "God curse such vile people," he said,
"for there's not a man of learning among them." I asked him how
and why he could say such a thing of a place where there were so
many learned men, and he, very angrily, replied: "Learned? I'll tell
you, sir, how learned they are. For fourteen years I was sacristan in
Majalahonda. Not once did they give me a prize in the public
contests for my songs and carols for Corpus Christi and Christmas.
To show you the wrong they did me, sir, I shall read them to you.

I know you'll enjoy them." And so, saying and doing, he unrolled a whole sheaf of noxious poems. From the first one, which I'll repeat here below, you can judge what the rest must have been like:

> *Shepherds, is it not great fun to say*
> *Today's Saint Corpus Christi's day?*
> *This is a day of joyous dances*
> *When the tiny lamb so young*
> *Shall hear his timely mourning sung,*
> *While with our cheer and making merry*
> *Soon the little lamb we bury*
> *Tucked into our tender gut.*
> *So sound away the gay sackbut*
> *And lead us on our happy way.*
> *Shepherds, is it not great fun to say, etc.*

"What more," he said to me, "could the very inventor of verse have said any finer than this? Just reflect on the mysteries the word 'shepherds' holds. Why it took me a month to study out ways to fit it in."

I couldn't hold back my laughter any longer for it was bubbling up and crowding out of my very nose and eyes. Letting out a great guffaw, I said: "A fine thing! Only I observe that you call him Saint Corpus Christi, and Corpus Christi is not a saint but the day of the commemoration of the Blessed Sacrament."

"What a fine thing to say!" he retorted making fun of me. "I'll show you on the calendar he's canonized." He said he'd wager his head on it.

I couldn't keep on I was so convulsed with laughter at this great ignorance. But before that, I told him the rhymes were worthy of any prize, and that I had never read such witty verses in my life before. "No?" he said quickly, "Well, listen to an extract of the book I have written to the eleven thousand virgins. To each and every one of them I have dedicated fifty verses. A delightful thing."

To excuse myself from listening to so many millions of verses, I begged him not to recite anything divine. So he began to read a comedy that consisted of more acts than the road to Jerusalem has miles. He commented: "I wrote it in two days and this is only the rough draft." It was about a hundred and twenty-five sheets long. The title was *Noah's Ark*. The action concerned cocks, rats, donkeys,

foxes and wild boars as in the fables of Aesop. I praised the form and the plot, to which he answered: "It is a thing of my own, but no other of its like is to be found on earth, and the novelty is greater than anything else. If I get it presented on the stage, it will be famous."

"How could it be presented," I asked him, "if the animals themselves do the acting and they can't speak?"

"That's the difficulty. If it weren't for that, could anything be more sublime? However, I thought of doing it all with parrots, thrushes and magpies that talk, and of putting monkeys on for the entr'actes."

"For certain, truly sublime." I said to him.

"I have written others even more sublime," he went on, "for the woman I love. Look here at these nine hundred one sonnets and twelve quatrains (he sounded as if he were reckoning *escudos* for *maravedís*) dedicated to the lady's legs."

I asked him if he had inspected these beauties. He answered that he hadn't because he was a clergyman, but that his sonnets were written in a spirit of prophecy. I confess truthfully that although I was amused to hear him, I was so frightened by the thought of so many bad verses that I began to turn the conversation to other subjects. I told him I saw some hares; "Well, then, I'll begin with a verse where I compare the lady's legs to that animal," and start he did. To divert him from his recitation, I said to him: "Sir, do you see that star shining there in broad daylight?" To which he answered: "When I finish this one, I'll recite you the thirtieth sonnet, in which I compare my lady to a star. Indeed you seem to know the structure of the poem." I felt depressed to find that it was impossible to name anything about which he hadn't composed some nonsense. Therefore, when I saw that we were approaching Madrid, I could hardly hold back the joy I felt, thinking that he would have to shut up if only from shame. It was just the contrary, for, to publicize his profession, he raised his voice as soon as we entered the town. Begging him to be quiet I explained to him that if any of the neighborhood boys got wind that he was a poet, there wouldn't be a scrap of garbage that wouldn't take after us. I explained that all poets had been declared crazy in a proclamation prepared by a man who had formerly been one and who had been reformed. My companion was very upset and asked me to read the document if

I had a copy. I promised to do so when we reached the inn. We came to the one where he usually stayed, and where before the door stood more than a dozen blind men. Some recognized my companion by his odor and others by his voice. They all gave him a noisy welcome. He gave all of them a slap on the back. After that some of them began to ask him for a prayer to the Just Judge composed in a grave and sententious verse, one that would bring out people's sense of charity. Others asked for prayers for souls; and so they went on, the poet receiving from each one eight *reales* as a down payment. He bid them goodbye and said to me: "Those blind men will be worth more than 300 *reales* to me. So if you will excuse me, sir, I'll go to myself for a bit to write some of their verses. After dinner we can hear the proclamation." Oh wretched life! None is more so than the life of those lunatics who live off poor wretches.

Chapter X

CONCERNING WHAT I DID IN MADRID AND WHAT
HAPPENED ON THE WAY TO CERCEDILLA
WHERE I SPENT THE NIGHT

The poet went off to himself to get his heresies and nonsense ready for the blind men. Meanwhile the supper hour arrived. We ate, and then he asked me to read him the proclamation. Since I had nothing else to do, I took it out and read it to him. I am inserting it here because it seemed so clever to me and so exact in the things it reproached. It was as follows:

Proclamation against addle-brained, insipid and
tasteless poets

This gave the clergyman a hearty laugh, and he said: "You might have said so before! By the Lord, I understood this concerned me, but it's only against poets without good taste." I found it very amusing to hear him talk as though his poetry were some fine vintage wine. Omitting the prologue, I began with the first article which read:

"Being cognizant of the fact that this species of vermin known as poets are our neighbors and Christians, though bad ones; seeing that throughout the year they worship eyebrows, teeth, ribbons, and slippers, and commit other more grievous sins, we hereby ordain that during Holy Week, all publicly known and street-corner poets be gathered together as is done with bad women, and that they be informed of their erroneous ways and be converted. To this end, we do hereby set aside houses for repentant poets.

"*Furthermore*, taking notice of the great heat there is in the canicular and the nightless couplets of the sun poets — as dried out as raisins by all the suns and orbs that fill their works— we impose on them perpetual silence in all things pertaining to the heavens and fix certain months off-season for the muses, as for hunting and fishing, so that they won't be made extinct by such prolific use.

71

"*Furthermore*, due to the fact that that devilish sect of men condemned to write poetry of perpetual concepts, splitters of words and perverters of reason, has infected our womenfolk with the disease of poetry, we do hereby declare ourselves revenged through the evil we have done to the latter for what the first female did to us through Adam. Because of the poverty and want that infects the globe, we order that all the couplets of the poets be burned like old trimmings, so as to extract the gold, silver and pearls, since in most verses the ladies are fashioned from all sorts of precious things, like statues with feet of clay."

Here the clergyman could stand no more, and rising he said: "Enough; even to robbing us of our belongings! Don't go any further, sir, for I intend to appeal this case to the Pope himself. I'll spend my last cent to see it through. What a fine thing for me, a clergyman, to have to suffer such an affront. I shall prove that the ballads of the ecclesiastical poets are not subject to such a proclamation and then I want to go settle it before the authorities." Partly, I felt like laughing, but to avoid wasting time—for it was getting late—I said to him: "Sir, this proclamation was prepared in fun, and has neither force nor judicial compulsion for lack of legal authority." "The Lord forgive me," he said, very upset. "You might have spared me, sir, so great a torment. Do you know, sir, what it is for a man who has composed eight hundred thousand verses to hear such a thing? Continue, sir, and may the Lord forgive you for giving me such a fright." I went on saying:

"*Furthermore*, we observe that half of what they say they owe to the holy water font as being untrue. They only tell the truth when they have something bad to say concerning one another.

"*Furthermore*, having observed that they have all banished good sense to the Valley of Jehosaphat, we do ordain that they shall be pointed out publicly throughout the land and that the violent ones shall be bound up. Moreover, they shall be accorded all the privileges of madmen and thus if they should get into mischief, and state and can offer proof that they are poets, not only shall they not be punished for their act, but they shall be commended for not having done more harm.

"*Furthermore*, having observed that since many poets have ceased to write Moorish ballads—although they still preserve certain remnants of them—they have turned to pastoral verse, and that, as a consequence, the cattle are thin from imbibing their tears, scorched in the flames of their loves, and so enraptured with the sound of their music that they no longer graze, we do ordain that poets shall leave that occupation, and that those who are friends of solitude shall become hermits, and the rest—since it is lively work and abounding in obscene expressions—shall devote themselves to mule tending."

"Some fairy, pimp, cuckold, or Jew (he shouted out), is responsible for this, and if I knew who he was, I would write him a satire that would fix him or anyone else who saw it for good and all. Imagine what a beardless man like myself would do in a hermitage, or a priest and keeper of communion wine as a mule tender! Ay, sir, such thoughts grieve me greatly."

"I've already told you, sir," I answered him, "that it's all a joke and that you should take it as such." Then I went on:

"Furthermore, in order to prevent further extensive plagiarisms, we do ordain that no verses be transmitted from Italy to Spain, nor from Aragon to Castile. As a penalty for violators, any guilty poet must dress himself decently. If he backslides, he must keep himself clean for a whole hour."

This amused the old man greatly for he himself wore a cassock so old it had turned grey from use, and so heavy with dirt that to bury himself, he would have had only to fold it over himself. His cloak was in such a terrible state he could have provided fertilizer for a couple of farms.

Half laughing, I told him the paper further ordained:

"that all women who fall in love with men whose stated profession is poetry, be classed with those insane persons who hang themselves or throw themselves over a cliff (and, due to this, they shall not be buried in consecrated ground).

"Furthermore, noting the great harvest of quatrains, songs, and sonnets that have appeared during these fertile poetry years, we do ordain that all bundles of these poems which are found unsuitable for use as wrapping paper in the grocers' shops, be shipped off to the privies without further ado."

I finally came to the last section which goes as follows:

"But observing in our mercy that there exist in our land three types of people so terribly wretched that they can't live without poets, that is to say, actors, blind men and the clergy, we do ordain, therefore, that a few poets shall be permitted to profess their art, provided they obtain a license from the of-

ficial censor of their home town. Those who serve actors shall
have certain limitations. They may not end their farces with
fisticuffs nor with devils on stage, nor end their plays with a
marriage. They may not fill out their plot with documents and
proclamations. Those who work for the blind shall not always
talk of happenings in Tetuan. They shall say "the present work"
and not "thuh presn wuk"; they shall banish from use such
overworked words as "Christian love," "brotherly," and "point
of honor." Those who write for the clergy shall avoid the use
of such names as Gil or Pascal and shall not make any puns on
words nor make up such loose verses that they can be changed
around to use over and over again.

"In conclusion, we do ordain that all poets in general stop
their use of Jupiter, Venus, Apollo, and other gods, under pain
of having to take these pagans for lawyers on their Judgment
Day."

Everyone who heard the document was delighted beyond words
and begged me for copies of it. Only the old priest swore by the
life of his holy prayers, *introibo* and *kyries*, that it was a satire
against him personally. He thought this because of what was said
about the blind men and added that he knew what was to be done
better than anyone else. Finally he said: "I am a man who has
stayed in an inn with the poet Liñán and have eaten more than a
couple of times with the famous author Espinel." He swore that
once in Madrid he had stood as close to the great Lope de Vega
as he was standing to me. Moreover he had seen Don Alonso de
Ercilla a thousand times, and had a portrait of the "divine" Figueroa
in his house. He had even bought some trousers the poet Padilla had
discarded when the latter became a monk and was still wearing
them even though they were in bad condition. He showed them to
us and set us into such gales of laughter that we didn't want to
leave the inn.

It was, however, already two o'clock and since we had to get
on our way, we set out for Madrid. Although I felt bad to do so, I
said goodbye to the old fellow and began to walk towards the city
gate.

To keep me from dawdling along in idle thoughts, the good Lord
placed a soldier in my path. Soon we struck up a conversation. He
asked me if I had just been in the capital. I replied that I had been
there just passing through.

"I'm in no mood to hear more," he said. "By God, I'd rather
be in a seige with snow up to my waist, armed to the teeth and on

a diet of wood, than to suffer the wiles they practice on honest men." I told him that he should realize that there were all kinds of people in the capital and that a man of fortune was always greatly respected.

"What respect," he said angrily, "for someone like me who has been waiting six months for a commission? And after twenty years of service and having shed blood in the King's service as these wounds testify!"

He showed me a scar of a hand's length on his groin which was, as clear as could be, no more than a swollen lymphatic gland. Then he pointed out two more souvenirs on his heels, explaining that they were from shots; I decided, because of two of my own that were exactly the same, that they came from chilblains. He took off his wide hat so I could see his face better: he had sixteen stitches on it which came, so he said, from a gash that had split open his nose. He had three other cuts that all together made him look like a map there were so many lines.

"These," he told me, "I received in Paris, in the service of God and the King, on whose behalf my face was carved up. I've received no more than a few fair words which they feel is recompense for the hell I went through. Now on your life, my fine scholar," he said, "never, by God, has any more remarkable man set foot on a battlefield."

He spoke the truth too, for he was so marked up he was indeed re-mark-able. He began to pull out some tin canisters and to show me papers which must have belonged to someone else whose name he had borrowed. I read them and said a thousand things to praise him, even remarking that neither the Cid nor Bernardo del Carpio had done what he had. At this he gave a start and said:

"What do you mean, 'done what I have'? By God, not even García de Peredes, Julián Romeros, or any others have! To hell with them! Why there wasn't any artillery in their time. By God, Bernardo wouldn't last an hour nowadays. You have only to ask, sir, in Flanders about the deeds of Señor Gappy and you'll see what they say."

"Is that you, sir?" I asked him.

He replied: "And who else? Don't you see the gap where my teeth are missing? But let's not talk about that for no man should sing his own praises."

With such talk, we went on our way until we came along side an emaciated old hermit dressed in brown and riding a donkey; he had a beard so long it trailed in the mud. We greeted him with the customary *Deo gratias* while he talked the praises of the fine wheat fields and the bountiful goodness of the Lord. The soldier, jumping forward, cried: "Ah, father! Why, I have faced lances thicker than those stalks of wheat, and by Christ's name, I did as well as I could in the sack of Antwerp, as God's my witness." The hermit admonished him not to swear so. The soldier answered: "It's plain to see, Father, that you've never been a soldier, for you scold me for practising my very own profession." I got a good laugh at seeing what he considered was soldierly and decided he must be a sort of knave, for among the military there is no custom so disliked by higher officers, if not by all soldiers, than that of swearing. We came to the slope of the pass: the hermit saying prayers on a rosary that was so much like a load of firewood carved into beads that with every Hail Mary there was a sound like a strike with a bowling ball. The soldier walked along comparing the rocks to castles he had seen. Then he would decide which place should be a strong point and where to put the artillery.

I walked along watching them. I was as frightened by the rosary of the hermit with its enormous beads as I was by the lies of the soldier.

"Oh, how I'd send a big part of this pass flying into the air with some gunpowder," he said, "and make a decent road for travellers!"

With this and other conversation we arrived at Cercedilla. It was already nightfall when the three of us entered the inn. We ordered some supper. Meanwhile the hermit said: "Let's chat for a bit, for idleness is the mother of vice. Let's play a game of Ave Marías." With that he let a playing card fall from his sleeve. I got a good laugh from that, remembering his beads. The soldier said: "Not unless we play a friendly game with stakes only up to the hundred *reales* I have with me." Since I felt greedy, I said I would play as many more. The hermit, so as not to make a bad showing, accepted our offers, and said that he had with him oil for the lamps which amounted to about two hundred *reales*. I confess I thought I'd be the wise owl [to drink it all in], but may the infidel Turks have as much luck with their plans as I had with mine. The game we played was landsquenet. The good part of it all was that the hermit said he didn't know how to play and for us to teach him. The blessed man let us win two hands, and then he gave us such a beating that he left not a cent on the table. He took his inheritance while the heirs were still alive. The old thief swept it all up with hands like a croup; it was sad to see. He always lost when the betting was light, and won when it got heavy. With every deal the soldier would let out a dozen "I-swears," and as many "I'll-be-damned's" interspersed with "by-the-life-of's." I sat biting my nails while our monk kept his busy raking in all my money. There wasn't a saint he didn't invoke. Our cards were like the Messiah [for the Jews], who never had come, but was still being awaited. We wanted to play on security but—after winning six hundred *reales* from me, which was every cent I had, and a hundred from the soldier—said that it was only for amusement and that since we were all brothers, there was no need to go on.

"Don't swear," he said to us, "for it was only because I entrusted myself to the Lord that things went so well for me." Not knowing the skill he exercised between the fingers and the wrist, we believed him. The soldier swore never to play again, and I the same.

"Confound it," said the poor second lieutenant (for he had told me his rank)—I've been with Lutherans and Moslems but never before have I suffered such a plundering."

The hermit just laughed at all this. He took out his rosary again to pray, while I, who had nothing left, asked him to give me enough to pay for supper and to pay the lodging for the two of us till we got to Segovia. We were both *in puribus,* stripped. He promised to do so. The hermit then crammed seventy [sic] eggs down his gullet. I've never seen the like in all my life. Then he said he was off to bed. We all slept in the same room where other people were sleeping too, for the regular rooms had already been taken. I stretched out feeling very sad. The soldier called the innkeeper and entrusted to him his papers in their tin canisters and a bundle of shirts long past the age of retirement. We got into bed. The father crossed himself and we in turn took our blessing from him. He fell asleep but I stayed awake and plotted how to get the money from him. The soldier talked in his sleep of the hundred *reales* as if they were gone for good.

When morning came, I quickly called for a light to be brought. After it had been brought, the innkeeper returned the soldier's bundle, but forgot the papers. The poor lieutenant shook the house with his cries demanding chamber service. The innkeeper got rattled and as we all told him to bring them for us, he hurried away at a run and brought back three chamber pots and said: "Here's one for each of you. Do you need more chamber service?" He had understood from the shouting that we had a case of loose bowels. Then things really began. The soldier jumped out of bed in his nightshirt and began to chase the innkeeper with his sword. He swore he would kill him for daring to make fun of him, a soldier who had fought at Lepanto, San Quintín and other battles, by bringing him a chamber pot instead of the papers he had entrusted to him. We all ran after him to hold him back, but couldn't. The innkeeper

77

said: "But sir, you asked for chamber service, sir. How am I supposed to know that you wanted me to bring your papers to you?"
We calmed them down and went back to the room. The hermit,
feeling suspicious of us, got back into bed saying that the fright had
upset him. He paid our bill and we left town by the pass, feeling
vexed by the behavior of the hermit and to see that we hadn't been
able to pry our money away from him.

We met a Genoese—I mean one of those Antichrists of Spanish
money—coming up the pass followed by a page shading him with a
parasol, all in a very moneyed way. We began to talk with him, but
he turned every conversation to cash, for his is a people that truly
are born for the purse. He started to talk about Besançon, and
whether or not he should give Besançon money. Finally the soldier
and I asked him who the fellow was he was referring to. This he
answered with a laugh: "It's an Italian city where businessmen
(there we are called the 'crooks of the pen') come together to fix
the value of money." From all this we supposed that in Besançon
they set the tune for the musicians with a gilded string attached. He
entertained us on the way by telling us how he had lost on a deal
into which he had put more than 60,000 *escudos*. He swore all this
on his conscience, although I think that conscience in businessmen
is like a maidenhead among whores: it's still being sold long after it's
gone. Hardly any of this type seem to have any; they must have
been told that it takes very little to make one's conscience hurt.
Consequently they leave it behind with the umbilical cord at the
time of birth.

We chatted on like this till we reached the walls of Segovia.
They brought joy to my eyes in spite of the memories which, including what had happened with Cabra, might well have made me
sad. Just as we got to the town, I saw the quartered remains of my
father strewn along the road, lying waiting to be carted in sacks to
Jehosaphat [to await Judgment Day]. I felt deeply moved. I returned to the town quite different from what I was when I left;
now I had a beard and was well dressed. I left my companions
and began to consider who in the town might be best acquainted
with my uncle (apart from the gallows) but I found no one of whom
I could inquire. I went up to several people to ask for Alonso
Ramplón but no one could tell me about him, and said they didn't
know him. I was happy to find that there were so many honest men
in the community, when, just as I was mulling over all this, I heard
the town crier play herald to the lash, and my uncle at work. Along
came a procession of men stripped to the waist, their heads uncovered, walking in front of my uncle. He was laying it on thick

78

with the lash he held in his hand, playing a tune on the ribs of five human harps whose cord-strings were made of strong ropes. Suddenly as I stood watching all this (beside a man to whose questions I had replied that I was a high-born gentleman), I saw my dear uncle. When his eyes fell on me, he ran up to me, throwing his arms around me and calling me nephew. I thought I would fall dead of shame. I didn't even turn around to say good-bye to the man I had been standing with. I went off with my uncle who said to me: "You can come along with me while I finish this bunch off. We're already on our way back to the jail and tonight you eat with me." I was on horseback and felt so beaten myself I'd have fit right into the line, so I told him I would wait for him there. I went my way feeling so ashamed that if it hadn't been for collecting my inheritance, I'd never have spoken to him again in my life nor even have been seen again in the place.

He finished his massage of the prisoners' shoulders and returned to take me to his house where we had something to eat.

CHAPTER XI

CONCERNING THE HOSPITALITY OF MY UNCLE AND HIS
VISITORS; THE COLLECTING OF MY INHERITANCE
AND MY RETURN TO THE CAPITAL

My dear uncle had his lodging next to a slaughterhouse in the home of a water carrier. As we were going inside, he said to me: "My home's no palace, but I promise you, nephew, that it's very well located for my business affairs." As we climbed the stairs I kept wondering what would happen to me at the top, if my climb really differed from mounting up to the gallows. We entered a room whose ceiling was so low that we went around with our heads bowed like people receiving benediction. My uncle hung up his lash on one of a line of pegs from which were hanging ropes, lariats, carving knives, meat hooks and other tools of his trade. He asked me why I didn't take off my cloak and sit down. I answered that I wasn't accustomed to doing so. God knows how ashamed I felt to see what an infamous fellow this uncle of mine was. He told me I had been lucky to run into him on such a happy occasion because we would dine well, as he had invited in some friends. Just then through the door came a man in a long purple cloak that hung down to his feet. He was one of those persons who beg money for souls in Purgatory. He rattled his collection box and then he said: "My souls have been worth as much to me today as your whippings to you. Put a coin in the box." They gave each other a chuck under the chin. The soulless old beggar then rolled up his robe until his bowed legs and underdrawers showed. Then he began to dance about and asked if Clemente had come. My uncle had no sooner said no than, wrapped in a hood and dirty as sin, in came a flute player of the acorn type, I mean swineherd. I knew what he was from the horn in his hand which—pardon my saying so—would have been more in style if he had worn it on his head. He greeted us after his fashion. With him entered a mulatto, left-handed and cross-eyed, wearing a hat with a brim with more slope than the side of a mountain, and a crown the height of a walnut tree. He also had on a sword with more trappings than there are hawks at a king's hunting party, and a doublet of suede. His face was like needlepoint because of the scars he had to

80

have stitched up. He came in and sat down, greeted everyone, and said to my uncle: "I swear, Alonso, that Romo [Flat-nose] and Gairoso [Sharp-paw] have paid their way today." The beggar jumped up and said: "I gave four *ducados* to Flechilla [Arrowhead] the hangman in Ocaña, to hurry up the mule and to use the light-weight lash when he was whipping me."

"Lord bless us!"—said the constable—"I paid Lobrezno too much in Murcia. That donkey crept along at a snail's pace and the scoundrel laid on till every spot of my back was in welts." The swineherd shrugged his shoulders and said: "My back is still virgin."

"Every dog has his day," commented the beggar. "I feel proud of myself," said my dear uncle, "for of all those who wield the whip, I give the best value for what I'm paid. Sixty *reales* they gave me today, so they got off with a few friendly strokes from the small whip."

Seeing what honorable people my uncle gathered around him, I confess that I began to blush so strongly that I couldn't hide my shame. The constable saw me and said: "Is this the holy father who underwent the stroking of his behind?" I retorted that I wasn't the type to undergo lashings. With that my uncle arose and said: "This is my nephew, a graduate of Alcalá and a person of position." They begged my pardon and tried to be polite. I was dying for some food, to collect my inheritance and to get away from my uncle.

They set the table. Then, on a rope to which a hat was hung (just as alms are collected in prison), they hauled up the meal from a cheap chop-house at the rear of the dwelling. In came the food, dished up on bits of plates and pieces of pans and jugs. No one could imagine what feelings of disgust I felt. They sat down to eat, the beggar at the head of the table and the others where they wished. I won't say we ate, except that it all seemed something for us to drink. The constable drank up three mugs of red wine and made it a toast to my health. I drank his health in watered wine. The swineherd drank more toasts than the rest of us all together. No one even thought of water, much less asked for it.

Five four-penny meat pies were served. Taking up a holy water sprinkler, after having taken off the top crust, they all said a responsory for the dead and a *requiem aeternam* for the souls of those whose flesh this was. My uncle said: "You'll remember now what I wrote you about your father." Indeed I did. The others ate, but I took only some of the crust, and that has been my habit ever since; always after that whenever I eat meat pie, I say a prayer for its departed soul.

81

They finished off more wine, which made over two gallons. So it was that the constable and the beggar were so tipsy by then that when a platter of sausages which looked like black fingers was brought in, one of them asked why roast punks were being served. My uncle was already so drunk that stretching out his hand and taking a sausage, he said (his voice had become rasping and hollow, and his eyes were swimming in wine): "Nephew, I swear on this food which God created in the image and likeness of Himself, I've never eaten better in all my life." Meanwhile, when I saw that the constable reached out, took the salt cellar, and said: "This is hot soup," and that the swinehard took a fist full of salt saying: "This is good for creating a thirst," then popped it all into his mouth, I began to laugh out of one side of my mouth and to foam at the other. They brought in more soup in a bowl which the beggar took between both hands and exclaimed: "God has blessed cleanliness." As he raised it to sip a bit, he missed his mouth and put it to his cheek. Then he tilted it, scalding himself and covering himself with soup from top to bottom in a most disgraceful way. When he saw what condition he was in, he tried to get up, but since his head felt so heavy, he put both hands on the table (which was shaky anyway) for support and completely overturned it. He splashed all the others. Then he said that the swineherd had pushed him. The swineherd, on top of whom he had fallen, got to his feet and picked up his horn and gave him a good whack. They began to fight, and while at close quarters, the beggar bit the swineherd on the cheek. This, added to the quarreling and rolling about, caused the latter to vomit up all he had eaten, right in the beggar's face. My uncle, who was a bit more sober than the rest, asked who had brought so many clergymen to his house. I could see that things were indeed doubling up and put a stop to the brawl. I separated the two of them and helped the constable up from the floor, where he had been weeping as sad as could be. I hustled my uncle off to bed, but not until after he had made a bow to a wooden candlestick he took for one of his guests. I took the horn from the swineherd, who, although the others were already asleep, wouldn't be quiet. He kept telling me to give him the horn, for no one had ever been able to get the tunes from it he could. He said he wanted to play with an organ accompaniment. At any rate, I watched them till they were fast asleep.

I then left the house and spent the afternoon walking around my old home town. I passed by Cabra's house where I heard the news that he had died of hunger. I returned to the house that evening four hours later. I found one of the guests awake and crawling around the room on all fours in search of the door and saying he couldn't find his house. I helped him to his feet. The others I let sleep until eleven that night when they awakened and began to stretch. My uncle asked what time it was. The swineherd, who still hadn't slept off his drunk, answered that it wasn't late, only siesta time, and that it was very sultry. The alms collector asked, as clearly as he could, for his collection box. Once he had it he said:

"Those souls are fortunate indeed to have my support in their charge." Then he started to leave, but instead of going out by the door of the room, he went to the window. When he saw the stars, he began to call the others at the top of his voice saying that the stars were out in mid-afternoon and that there was a tremendous eclipse going on. They all made the sign of the cross and kissed the floor. When I saw the knavery of the beggar, I was scandalized and decided then and there to keep away from such men. The base conduct and infamy that I witnessed made me more and more desirous of the company of gentlemen and other decent people. One by one, I took care of them all, as well as I could. My uncle, although he wasn't completely out-foxed, was still not too foxy. I made myself comfortable on a pile of clothes, some of which were my own and others which belonged to those who had already passed into God's keeping.

In that way we passed the night. In the morning I talked with my uncle about getting my inheritance. He had awakened saying he felt as if he'd been through the mill, but didn't know why. The room—both from the rinsing given it by the drunkards and from the water they'd loosed during the night—was turned into a pool. Finally when my uncle got up, we talked for quite a while about my affairs. It was hard work for me because the man was such a drunkard and boor. Eventually I got him to give me an accounting of part of the inheritance, though not all of it, and so he gave me some 300 *ducados*. My good father had earned them with his own sensitive hands and left them in charge of a virtuous lady under whose guidance goods were stolen for some ten leagues around. So as not to weary you, sir, I'll just say that I received and pocketed what money my uncle hadn't drunk up, which was no small amount. The reason was that he thought I would graduate with the money and through my studies would one day wear the cardinal's red on my back. His own hands had made so many backs red that he saw no reason why I should not easily do the same. Seeing I had the money, he said to me: "Son Pablos, it will be your own fault if you don't prosper and be a good man, for you have an example before you. You have money and I shall never fail you; what I make and have is yours." I thanked him very much for his offer. We passed the rest of the day in foolish conversation. That evening my uncle and the swineherd played cockal [a game played with a knuckle-bone], while the beggar played his mass money as if it were destined for something else. It was a sight to behold the way they tossed up that cockal. The one who'd thrown it up in the air would catch it and balance it on his wrist. Then he'd toss it again. The cockal served just as well as their cards. Both whetted their thirst and the jug stayed in their midst. When night fell they left. My uncle and I went each to his own bed, for by now he had provided me with a mattress. At daybreak I got up before he awoke and left unnoticed by him and went to an inn. I locked the door on the outside as I went out and threw the key down a cat-hole. Thus, I went to an inn where I could hide and await the opportunity to go to the capital. I left a letter in my uncle's room and in it explained my departure and the reasons for it. I also warned him not to follow me because I hoped never to see him again.

CHAPTER XII

CONCERNING MY DEPARTURE AND THE ADVENTURES
I HAD ON MY WAY TO THE CAPITAL

That morning a muleteer was leaving the inn with a load of things for the capital. He had a donkey which he hired out to me. I went ahead to await them outside the town gate. When he got there I mounted the ass and the day's journey began. As we went along, I said to myself: "There you'll remain, my villainous uncle, a disgrace to all good folk, you saddler of windpipes."

I was thinking that here I was on my way to the capital where no one knew me — which was the thing that consoled me most — and where I would get ahead through my own efforts. Once there, I intended to doff my student outfit and put on short, fashionable clothes. But let's return to the doings of my uncle who was very much offended by my letter which went as follows:

Señor Alonso Ramplón:
Since God Almighty has shown me such singular mercies — in depriving me of my worthy father and keeping my mother in Toledo, where at least she will go up in smoke — I lacked only the pleasure of seeing done unto you what you have done to so many others. I aspire to be Number One of my line, as to be Two is impossible unless I fall into your hands, sir, and am carved up as you've done to so many others. Do not inquire for me as I intend to deny our blood relationship. Serve God and the King.

It would be too much to guess at the blasphemies and curses he must have uttered against me. But let's return to my journey. I was mounted on a dapple-grey donkey that came from La Mancha. I hoped I would not meet anyone on the way. Suddenly at a distance I saw a gentleman coming at a quick pace. He was jauntily wearing a cape and sword. He had on tight breeches and boots, a fashionable ruff collar, and his hat turned up on one side. I suspected that he was a nobleman who had walked ahead of his coach. Therefore when I came abreast of him, I greeted him. He looked at me and said:

85

"You are, no doubt, my young college friend, much more comfortable on that donkey's back than I here with all my equipment."

Taking this to refer to his coach and servants which he had left behind, I said:

"To tell the truth, sir, I find this an easier way to travel than by coach because — although you may ride in luxury in the one you've left behind you — the jolts are quite upsetting.

"What coach behind?" he said excitedly.

Then, turning to look back, his sharp movement caused his one and only cord suspender to break, and down fell his pants. Though he saw I was dying with laughter, he asked me to give him a hand. When I saw that there was no more to the shirt than a tail end and that the rear of his trousers covered no more than half of what they should, I said to him:

"Good Lord, sir, if you can't wait for your servants, I can't help you because I too have only one piece of cord."

"If you are making fun of me, sir," he said while he held his breeches up with his hand, "very well, for I don't understand what you mean about servants."

He enlightened me so — on matters of how poor he was — that after a half-league's journey he told me that if I didn't do him the favor of letting him ride on the donkey a while, he would never be able to go on to the capital. He was that tired from holding up his breeches. Moved to pity, I alighted, and since he couldn't get his trousers straightened out, I had to help him to mount. I was astonished at what I discovered when I boosted him up: his whole behind, which was hidden by the long cape, had no more covering than a lining of bare buttock. He realized what I had seen and tactfully forestalled my remarks by saying:

"Good student, all is not gold that glitters. You must have thought when you saw my fine collar and my imposing figure that I was the Duke of Arcos or the Count of Benavente. These fancy trimmings serve to hide from the world what you have just touched."

I assured him that I had been led to believe that things were quite different from what they looked.

"Well, sir, you haven't seen anything yet," he went on, "for all I have is clear to be seen. I have nothing to hide. I appear to you to be a gentleman in every respect, with a family manor and a mountain retreat, which if it sustained me as I do my nobility, would leave me no cause for complaint. However, my educated friend, good blood can't be sustained without bread and meat, and by God's mercy, blood is red in every man's veins. Nevertheless, a man can't be a somebody when he has nothing. I have already

86

found out the worth of my letters-patent of nobility. One day when I had nothing to eat, they wouldn't give me a couple of slices of meat in a chop house for them. As if the letters weren't gold. It would be more beneficial to use the gold on pills where it would be worth more than on letters. After all, few letters are gold. I've even sold the land for my grave, and so have not even a place to drop dead. The estate of my father, Don Toribio Rodríguez Vallejo Gómez de Ampuero — he possessed every one of those names — was lost as bail. Only my title of "Don" has been left to me to sell. So far I haven't had the luck to find anyone who has need of it. These days the person who can't use it preceding his name finds it attached to the end. Just look at mastodon, myrmidon, outdone, overdone, and the like.

I must confess that although I had many a laugh as the gentleman talked, his troubles touched me. I asked him what his name was and where he was headed. He replied that he had all of his father's names: Don Toribio Rodríguez Vallejo Gómez de Ampuero y Jordán. Such a high-sounding name had quite a ring, for with its ending on "dán" and its beginning on "don," it had the sound of the toll of a bell. Finally my companion said that he was going to the capital because the penurious nobleman like himself quickly finds himself ostracized in a small town. There was no way to make a livelihood. For that reason he was off to the common haven for men like him, where there was room for all and free meals for the stomach that dared. "When I'm in that city, I never want for a hundred *reales* in my purse, a bed, food, and a healthful turn through the park. In the capital, ingenuity is like a philosopher's stone which turns to gold whatever it touches."

I had visions of clear sailing. As a sort of entertainment for the journey, I asked him to tell me how, with whom and in what way people like himself who didn't have a thing were able to live. I asked this because it seemed a difficult thing to do in times such as these when people aren't content with just their own belongings, but covet those of others as well.

"There are many people of that kind, my son," he said, "and many of another. In my case, flattery is the master key which opens the doors in such cities. You'll find what I'm telling you more credible if you listen to what has happened to me and my projects; you'll soon put aside any doubts."

CHAPTER XIII

IN WHICH THE NOBLEMAN CONTINUES THE
NARRATION OF HIS LIFE AND HABITS

"The first thing you must know is that in the capital there are always the dumbest and the wisest, the richest and the poorest, and extremes of all kinds. Evil people are overlooked and the good are unrecognized. There are classes of people (like myself) whose origins, possessions and family are unknown. Among ourselves we have several names: we call each other no-counts, addle-pates, counterfeits, dunghills, dieters, and hungry houn'dogs. Ingenuity is our mediator. Most of the time our stomachs go empty since it is quite a hard task to carry off a meal in another man's hands. We are on board at every banquet table. We are the moths of the chophouses and the uninvited guests. We subsist almost on the air itself and live rather contentedly. We are people who eat a leek and pretend it's a capon. Someone who comes to visit us in our homes finds the rooms full of chicken and mutton bones, fruit peelings, and the door piled up with hen and capon feathers and rabbit skins. We gather all this up in town while it's still dark; it makes an impressive display the next day. When a guest comes in we grumble: "Can't I ever get that girl to sweep the place clean? I hope to heaven, sir, that you will pardon all this. Last night a few friends dined with me here and the servants these days" . . . etc. Anyone who doesn't know us believes that it's true and thinks we're generous hosts.

"What shall I tell you about wangling a meal in other people's homes? Once we've spoken a few words to someone, we get his address. Then exactly at meal time and just as he's about to sit down at the table, we pretend that we stopped by for the pleasure of seeing our friend, for in understanding and wisdom his equal is not to be found. If he asks us if we have eaten, and the hosts have not already begun, we reply that we have not. If we get an invitation we don't wait for a second one. You see, he who hesitates may have a long fast. If the meal has begun, we say that we have eaten and then compliment the host on his skill as he carves up a fowl, a loaf of bread, a roast or whatever the platter may be.

This gives us the chance to gulp a mouthful as we say: 'Now, sir, you must let me play the butler for you. I remember when, God rest him in heaven, the (duke, marquis, or count of such-and-such) who was a great friend of mine would get more pleasure out of watching me carve than from eating.' Having said that, we take up the carving knife and cut off little tidbits. Finally we say: 'Oh, how good it does smell! It would be an insult to the cook not to try it. What talent he has! What wonderful seasoning.' With a bit of talking and doing, half the platter disappears in the sampling: the turnip as a delicacy, the bacon as a delight, and whatever else there is as our favorite dish. When this doesn't work, we can always get charity soup at some monastery. We don't eat it where we can be seen. We go out of sight and pretend to the monks that we come for the soup more out of piety than from necessity.

"You ought to see one of us in a gambling house, how carefully we serve the players and trim the candles, bring in chamber pots, fetch the playing cards and applaud the winner, all for one poor little *real*.

"We know by heart, in so far as our wardrobes are concerned, every old clothing shop. Just as in some places there is a fixed time for prayers, we have one when we darn. We're quite a sight in the morning. We are all declared enemies of the sun because he shows up our darning, stitches and patches. Nevertheless, we stand in his light with our legs apart, and that way we can detect from our own shadows on the ground any rags or shreds of cloth that hang down. Then we take up our scissors and shave off any whiskers on our pants. Since the cloth between the thighs always wears out so quickly, you should see how we whittle away at the back side to fill out the front. Usually by the time our sword play is done, the rear end has been pacified enough to stay as a patch where it should. Only our cloaks know what is going on. That's why we must stay on our guard on windy days or when we go up well-lighted stairways or get on a horse. We make studies of how to stand in certain types of light. On bright days we walk with our legs close together and make our bows from the ankles because if we bent our knees the needlework would show. Nothing we wear on our whole bodies has not been something else. Each piece has a history; *verbi gratia:* you see this doublet, sir. First it was a pair of broad breeches, the grandchild of a cape, and the great-grandchild of a hooded cloak; that was its beginning. Now it's about to become the foot in some stockings, among other things. Our slippers started out as handkerchiefs; they had once been towels and shirts, all of them the offspring of sheets. When they are too worn for anything else, we use them for writing paper, and finally we make of them a remedy for our shoes; I've seen many a pair raised from the dead by the use of this medication. Is there any need to explain why we keep away from the lamplight at night so that no one can see our bald short cloaks and beardless doublets? There is no more nap left on them than there is on a cobblestone, for though the good Lord gives us plenty of fuzz on our faces we have none on our capes. We avoid spending money on barbers too. We always wait until someone else has the need, and then we give each other a haircut. Thus we're in keeping with the saying in the Gospel: 'Help one another as if you were brothers.' [Moreover we always take care not to visit the houses that another one of us frequents if we know one is after the same objective as another.] What jealous stomachs we do have!

"We are obligated to ride publicly through the streets on a mount once a month even though it be on an ass, and to ride in a coach once a year even though it be on the driver's box or in the rear. If however we ride inside the coach, we make sure that we are right beside the door. Then we stick our heads out the window and bow so as to be seen by all; we call out to our friends and acquaintances even though they're not looking our way.

"If we have flea bites in the presence of ladies, we have a trick of scratching in public without being seen. If the bite is on the thigh, we relate the story of a soldier we saw run through from one side to the other and indicate with our fingers that part that itches, but scratching it rather than pointing it out. If this happens in church and the bite's in the chest, we do the *sanctus* though it be time for the *introibo*. If it's in the back, we get up and go over to a corner, where we pretend to try to observe something and scratch by rubbing against the wall.

"What could I say about lying? Truth never touches our lips. We include the names of dukes and counts in our conversations, some as friends and others as relatives, but always making sure that these same noblemen are either dead or far away. One very unusual thing is that we never fall in love unless it be to obtain our daily bread. You see, the order forbids genteel ladies, no matter how pretty they are. Consequently we go out on call, to the shopkeeper's wife for food, to the landlady for our lodging and to the laundress for starching our ruffed collars. Since we have little to eat and don't live very well, we have a hard time satisfying them all, but we take them by turns and make them all happy.

"How would anyone looking at these boots of mine think that they were riding my legs bareback without so much as a stocking between them and the skin? Would anyone looking at this collar think I had no shirt underneath? A gentleman can do without the rest, but must have his starched ruffed collar. First of all because it is an ornament which is becoming to the person, and second because after turning it a few times its starch will provide him with a meal, if he partakes of it with skill. You see, my educated friend, one of us has to get by with more mensal deficiencies than those of a pregnant woman in nine months. We live as well as we can in the capital. Sometimes we have money and are well off; at others, we are in the poorhouse. We do manage to live, however, and he who learns to shift for himself is a king no matter how little he has."

I had so enjoyed hearing the nobleman tell of these odd ways of life and had been so well entertained by it all that I walked on foot until we arrived at Las Rozas where we spent the night. My noble companion joined me for dinner. He hadn't a cent with him, and I felt myself under an obligation to him for his instructions. Through them my eyes had been opened about a lot of things, and most of all to the knavery I could get myself into. I told him my plans before we went to bed, and he threw his arms around me saying that he was delighted that his words had made an impression on so intelligent a youth. He offered to introduce me to the rest of his confreres in swindling in the capital, and to get me lodging with them. I accepted his offer, without however telling him the amount of *escudos* I had in my purse. I said that I had only a hundred *reales* with me. The sum was enough, plus the kindness I had shown and continued to show to him, to earn his friendship.

I bought my companion some leather laces with which he tied up his breeches. We slept out the night, got up early the next morning and went on our way to Madrid.

CHAPTER XIV

CONCERNING WHAT HAPPENED IN THE CAPITAL
BETWEEN THE TIME OF MY ARRIVAL
AND NIGHTFALL

We reached the capital at ten in the morning and dismounted before the home of Don Toribio's friends. We went up to the door and knocked. It was opened by a poorly dressed and very ancient old woman. My companion asked for his friends and the old lady answered that they had gone out to see what they could find on their usual search. We remained there alone until after twelve o'clock had struck; he passed the time telling me exciting tales about his half-priced way of life; I took in every word. At twelve thirty there came through the door a tall phantom who wore an outfit of baize that hung to his feet and more worn out than the man's sense of shame. The two chatted in thieves' slang. After that the newcomer gave me a pat on the back and offered me his friendship. When we had talked a bit, he pulled out a glove with sixteen *reales* in it, and a letter (it was a permit to collect alms for the poor) with which he had obtained the money. He emptied the glove out and pulled out the other. Then he folded the two together as a doctor does. I asked him why he didn't put them on and he replied that since they were both for the same hand they were good only for carrying.

All this time I noticed that he didn't take his cloak off, so I asked (being the newcomer that I was), why he remained muffled up. He answered: "Son, there's a hole down my back, and near that, a flannel patch and a grease spot. This piece of cover hides all that, and I can go out looking respectable." He took off the cloak and I saw that beneath his cassock he wore a sort of bundle. I thought it was his breeches, because the form was like them. However, before going in to be deloused, he tucked up his clothes, and I saw that there were two disks of pasteboard attached at the waist and fitted to the thighs so that they gave the appearance of breeches under the somber cloak. Actually he had neither shirt nor breeches on and was so naked there was hardly anything to delouse. He went into the room for delousing and so that no one else would come in, put up a little sign, similar to those that are used in sacristies, which said: "Delouse within." I gave thanks to the Lord when I realized how much ingenuity He had given to men, even though He deprived them of riches.

"As for me," my good friend said, "I've finished up the journey with a trouser-ache, so I'll be off to do some mending." He asked if there were any rags and the old woman (who went two days a week to gather up rags in the streets just as those women do who gather paper for treating the ills of gentlemen's soles) said no. She added that Don Lorenzo Iñiguez del Pedroso had already been confined to his bed for two weeks due to the shortage of rags.

We were conversing like this when in came a chap wearing riding boots, a gray suit, and a hat whose brim was turned up on both sides. He had heard about me from the others and spoke to me quite affectionately. He took off his cloak beneath which — who, sir, would have suspected it — he wore an outfit that was brown wool in front, white linen in back and all set against a background of sweat. I couldn't contain a laugh, but he said very tolerantly:

"You'll get used to such things and then you won't laugh. I'll bet you don't know why I wear this hat with the brim turned up."

I replied that it must be for elegance and to give an unobstructed view.

"To obstruct the view, you mean," he said, "because I haven't any hatband, and this way it can't be seen." After that he took out some twenty letters and as many silver *reales*. He said that he hadn't been able to deliver the letters, each of which carried a *real* of postage due. They were all written by my new friend who signed them with whosoever's name he happened to think of. He wrote various news to the most respectable citizens of the town, delivered them in that outfit and collected the postage due. He did this once a month. I found this novel way of life quite fascinating to behold.

Two other fellows came in just then. One wore a wool doublet that reached halfway down his breeches, and a cloak of the same cloth with the collar turned up so that the coarse linen, which was torn, could not be seen. His breeches were of camlet and consisted of no more than the parts which could be seen. The rest was made of red baize. This chap walked along arguing loudly with the other one. The latter wore a vandyke collar rather than the full ruff, and a shoulder belt hung with powder flasks as he had no cloak. He used a crutch and had one leg wrapped up in rags because he had only one stocking. He acted like a soldier. He had been one, though a bad one and only in the quietest sectors; he told many strange tales of his service, and under guise of a soldier's

93

privilege, went in where he pleased. The one with the doublet and the half-breeches said:

"You owe me half, or at least a good part of it. If you don't split up, I swear to God . . ."

"Don't swear to God," said the other, "because once we are home I'm no longer a cripple and can give you a good thrashing with this crutch."

With a you'll-give-it-to-me and an I'll-do-no-such-thing and the usual accusations of lying, they grabbed each other. They ended up with their hands full of rags after the very first tug. We made peace between them and asked what had caused their quarrel. The soldier replied:

"So you try your tricks on me? You won't even get half. Let me tell you gentlemen that today when we were in Holy Savior's Church, a child came up to this poor devil and asked him if I was Lieutenant Juan de Lorenzana. He said that I was, after he saw that the child was carrying something in his hand. He brought him up to me and (calling me lieutenant) said: 'Sir, this child wants to see you.' I understood of course, and said that I was the lieutenant. I got the message and a dozen handkerchiefs along with it. I sent a reply back to the mother who had obviously sent them to someone of that name. Now just ask me for your half. You can cut me to ribbons first. My very own nose will wear these handkerchiefs out."

The case was decided in his favor. He was, however, forbidden to blow his nose on them. He was ordered to take them to the old woman for the good of our little community. She could use them to make collars and cuffs which would make it appear that we were wearing complete shirts. Nose-blowing was forbidden in our little group, except when [using one's fingers] doing it into the air. Most of the time we just snuffed it up, which was both nutritious and economical. Thus the affair came to a close.

Night fell. We all went to bed together looking like knives in a sheath. Suppertime had come and gone unobserved. Most of the group didn't even undress. By going to bed wearing the same clothes they had worn all day, they complied with the old saying about sleeping in one's skin.

CHAPTER XV

IN WHICH THE SAME SUBJECT IS CONTINUED, AND
OTHER STRANGE ADVENTURES ARE TOLD

Morning came and we all armed for the day. I was already as
well established with the others as if we had all been brothers.
There is always an air of ease and comfort about things that are
bad. It was a sight to watch one of the men put on a shirt in twelve
different installments. The shirt was made from twelve different
rags. As each piece went on he said a prayer, like a priest getting
dressed for the mass. Another fellow kept losing his leg in the ins-
and-outs of his trousers; when he would find it again, it would be
in the wrong place. A third chap asked someone to help him put
his jacket on, for after half an hour he still hadn't determined
which way it went.

Once this was over, and what a sight it was, everyone took up
needle and thread for the purpose of doing some stitching. They
had to assume some very queer postures to patch up holes all over
themselves. [One, to whip up a hole beneath his arm, twisted himself into an L. Another, down on his knees, did his patching doubled
up like a 5; he was giving aid to his stockings. Another man who
wanted to fasten on his knee-pads put his head between his knees
and he formed a perfect oval. Not even Bosch ever painted the
strange postures I saw there.] The old woman handed them their
raw materials of rags and left-over bits of tattered cloth of different
colors which the soldier had brought home. When the Mending
Hour—for that was what they called it—had come to an end, they
walked about inspecting one another for any place that was badly
repaired. They all decided to go out. I told them that I wanted them
to plan out my clothes since I wished to spend a hundred *reales* on
a new outfit and get rid of my student uniform. "Not that," they
all said. "That money goes to the common fund. Let's dress him
from the reserves and assign him a diocese in the town where he
can explore and exploit for himself alone."

That seemed all right to me. I deposited my money, and in
an instant, they made a mourning coat of my student clothes and
shortened my cloak to make it look like the latest thing. What was

left over from it, they changed into an old hat re-dyed. They put some inkstand cotton around it for a band. They took off my collar and my trousers and in their place put on breeches slashed only in front. The sides and the rear were chamois skin. My halfhose of silk weren't even half. They only reached four inches below my knee, four inches that were covered by tight boots worn over the colored socks I had on. The collar was like grill work it was so torn. They put it on me, then advised me: "The collar is worn away in back and on the sides. Now, sir, if one person is looking at you, follow his gaze around as a sunflower does the sun; if two people are looking at you, one from each side, step backwards. For any-one behind you, always keep your hat turned down over the back of your neck so the brim will hide the collar and leave your fore-head bare. To anyone who asks you why you wear it that way, answer that you do so because an honest face is open to all."

They presented me with a box containing black and white thread, silk, cord, needles, a thimble, cloth, linen, satin, a few odds and ends and a knife. They thrust a packet into my belt; it was steel and a flint in a leather case. Then they said: "With this packet, you can go anywhere in the world without needing either friends or men in your debt. In this little box are all our remedies. Take it and keep it." They set aside the quarter of San Luis for me as a place to scavenge for my livelihood. Thus my day began by setting forth with all the others. Since I was a novice, they gave me as my sponsor (for my first exercises in swindling, just as they do a priest who says his first mass) the same fellow who had brought me to them and made the conversion.

We strolled out of the house, each holding a rosary, and set out for my newly-assigned district. We were courteous to all: to the men, we took off our hats, wishing all along we could take off their cloaks; to the ladies, we made deep bows, for women are always pleased with such things. My sponsor would say to one passer-by: "I'll have some money tomorrow," and to another, "Wait just one more day, sir. The bank has things tied up." One chap wanted his cloak back; another demanded his waistband. I began to realize that my sponsor was so close a friend to his friends that he owned nothing of his own. We zigzagged like a serpent from one sidewalk to the other to avoid the houses of his creditors. Already someone had asked him for rent for the house, another for rent on his sword, and still another, for the rent on sheets and shirts. I was beginning to see that my fine friend was "for rent" like some mule. It so hap-pened that he saw in the distance a man who—so he said—was tearing his very eyes out over a debt. In order to avoid being recognized, my companion let down his hair, which had been tucked up, back of his ears, with the result that he looked like a Nazarene, half Veronica and half wooly knight. Then he put a patch over one eye and began to talk to me in Italian. There was time to do all this while the other fellow approached us, for he hadn't seen us yet. He was too busy gossiping with some old crone. I'm telling the truth when I say that I saw the fellow walk around my friend like a dog getting ready to lie down. He made more signs of the cross than a sorcerer, then went on his way murmuring: "God bless me, I thought sure it was he! The man who loses his oxen thinks he hears cow bells ring in his ear." I was dying of laughter at the sight of my friend's face. He stepped into a doorway to straighten his hat and take off the patch, then he said: "These are tricks to avoid paying up debts. Remember, brother, you'll see a thousand things like this go on in this city."

We walked on and stopped at the corner. There, since it was morning, we had a couple of slices of preserved fruit and some brandy, a present made to us by a rascally woman who heartily greeted my sponsor. She then said to me: "With this much you won't have to worry about food today. At least you're sure of this." I was upset thinking that dinner was still so doubtful, and my stomach made its own reply. The woman answered: "You have little faith in the religion and order of the hungry. The good Lord doesn't fail either the crows or the blackbirds; not even the notaries. Why should he fail the starving? You don't have any guts!"

"That's true enough," I said, "but I'm afraid of having even less and nothing to fill them with."

While we were talking, a clock struck noon. Since I was new to these ways of doing, the preserved fruit did not fill me up. I was as hungry as if I had not eaten at all. The hour had struck a cord in my memory, and so I turned to my friend and said: "Brother, this acquaintance with hunger makes being a novice pretty hard. Man was made to eat more than we have, and here you've put me to fasting like a monk. The fact that you don't feel hungry proves nothing to me. Since you have been building up immunity to hunger since you were a child—like Mithridates and poison—you can subsist on what little you get. I don't see you making any great effort to exercise your teeth, so I've decided to do what I can about it myself."

"Bless my soul," he answered, "It's just struck noon and you're already in such a hurry? You are certainly punctual in your wants and their satisfaction. You need to use a little patience when you're off schedule. Just stuff yourself all day long! Why, that's no more than animals do! No one has ever heard tell that any of our group of gentlemen has ever had loose bowels. Our needs are so infrequently relieved that we don't have to relieve ourselves. I've already told you that God fails no one. If you're in such a hurry, I'll go to the soup kitchen of Saint Jerome's where the monks are as fat as milk-fed capons. There I'll fill my belly. If you care to, come along. And if not, everybody to his own taste."

"Goodbye," I said, "My needs are not so small that they can be filled with the leftovers of others. Each on his own way."

My companion walked off stiffly and looking down at his feet. He took out a few crumbs of bread (which he always carried on purpose in a little box) and scattered them over his beard and clothes so that he looked as if he had just eaten. I walked along picking my teeth now and then. I also wiped crumbs off my moustache and brushed them off my cloak in such a way that anybody seeing me would think I was well fed. If they had referred to my lice, they would not have been far wrong.

I had confidence in my gold *escudillos,* although it hurt my conscience to fall back on them when my innards were supposed to live freely. I came to the conclusion that I had to end my fasting. By this time, I came to the corner of the street of San Luis where a baker lived. There appeared before my eyes a large pie. When the odors of the oven struck me on the nose, I froze (though I kept on moving) like a hunting dog stalking a pheasant: my eyes were set on it, and I stared at it so that the pastry dried up like a child struck by the evil-eye. I stood there preparing my plans for carrying it off; then I resolved to pay for it. While I was trying to make up my mind, one o'clock struck. I was so depressed that I decided to go into one of the restaurants thereabout. Just as I started off for one, as God willed it, I ran into a friend of mine named Flechilla who had graduated with me. He came swaggering down the street with more pimples on his face than a sick man, and so many mud spots on him that he looked like a dung cart. He ran toward me when he saw me (indeed, the way I was dressed, it was something that he recognized me); I threw my arms around him, and he asked how I was. Then I said to him, "My dear sir, I have so many things to tell you! How sorry I am that I'm leaving tonight."

"I'm sory too," he said, "and if it weren't so late and I didn't have to hurry home to eat, I'd stop to talk longer. However, my married sister and her husband are waiting for me."

"What? Is Doña Ana here?" I cried. "Even if I have to drop everything, let's go. I want to pay my respects as I should."

My eyes opened wide when I heard he hadn't eaten. I went along with him and began to talk to him about a little lady (one he had liked a lot in Alcalá). I said that I knew her whereabouts and could arrange for him to get an invitation to her house. He was very much interested in my offer which was just part of the business of talking about things to please him. We continued our conversation until we arrived at his house. We went inside where I put on quite a show for his sister and brother-in-law. They, supposing that since I had come at such an hour I was, of course, invited, began to tell me that if they had known they were going to have a distinguished guest they would have prepared for the occasion. I took the opportunity to invite myself and said that I was one of the family and an old friend and that they would offend me by treating me with formality. They sat down and so did I. In order to make me feel better about my staying (not only had he not invited me; such a thing had not even passed through his mind), I would tell him more nonsense about the old girl friend now and then. I whispered to him that she had asked about him, and told him other lies. All of this helped him to accept with good grace the sight of my gluttonous stuffing. I made a bigger hole in the side of the first course than a cannon ball shot through a leather jacket. The soup was served and I downed it all in two mouthfuls. There was no malice involved, but the haste was so savage that it seemed that even when I had it between my teeth I still was not sure of the food. As God is my father, the earth of Valladolid cemetery does not disolve a body more quickly — it disintegrates them in twenty-four hours — than I demolished the day's food supply. It all disappeared with the speed of a special delivery. They surely must have noticed the savage gulps of broth I took and how I drained the soup tureen, and how I persecuted the bones and lay waste to the meat. To tell the truth, half-jokingly I even lined my pockets with leftover bread. When the table was cleared, my friend and I got up to talk about going to his old girl friend's house. I made it sound very easy. As we were chatting about this near a window, I pretended someone had called me from the street. I replied: "Are you calling me, Madam? I'll be right out." I excused myself and said that I would be back right away. He's still waiting for me to this very day. You see, I left as soon as the bread was eaten and the company dispersed. He ran into me many times after that, and each time I made excuses with a thousand different lies which aren't worth telling you here.

I wandered down the street and came to the Guadalajara gate. There I sat down on one of the benches that merchants have at their doors. It was God's will that just then up to the shop came two ladies, of the type that raise funds by the grace of their looks, muffled up to their eyes and accompanied by an old woman and a page. They inquired if there was any velvet with unusual trimming. I wanted to start a conversation, so I thought I'd try trick rhymes on the word velvet, silk net, beset, vignette; there wasn't one I didn't pull. I realized that my liberty had given them the right to some object in the shop, so like someone who undertakes an adventure without risk of loss, I offered them whatever they wanted. They haggled a bit saying that they never accepted gifts from persons they did not know. I took advantage of the situation to say that it had been very forward on my part to make them such an offer. I begged them to accept some cloth that I had received from Milan and which a page would bring them that night. (I pointed out as my own a page who was standing across the street with his cowl off waiting for his real master who was inside another shop). And so that the ladies would think I was a man of position and well-known, I raised my hat to every gentleman within hearing distance who passed by. I didn't know a single one of them, but I bowed my head as if I were on familiar terms with them. They were much impressed with all this. They were even more taken in when right in front of them I took out some hundred *escudos* of what I had with me on the pretext of giving alms to a beggar who had come up to me. They said it was time for them to go home as it was already late. They excused themselves, but not before warning me to have the page come very secretly. As a token of their favor and in a tone of jest, I asked them for a rosary with gold links which the prettier of the two was wearing. I asked for it as a pledge that I would see them the next day without fail. They hesitated to give it to me. I offered them the hundred *escudos* as a pawn. They told me where their house was, thereby hoping to fleece me more. Since they had confided in me, they asked where my lodging was. They said that a page couldn't come to their house at all hours as they were of the gentry of the town. I led them down the Calle Mayor. At the entrance of Carretas Street I picked out the finest and largest house I could see. There was a coach without horses standing in front of it. I said that this was my house and that coach and master were both at their service. I told them my name was Don Alvaro de Córdoba and into the front door I went, right before their eyes. I recall that as we left the shop I beckoned to one of the pages (with an air of great authority); I pretended to instruct him to wait for me there with the other pages. That is what I said I had said. The truth is that I asked him if he was the servant of my uncle, the

Comendador. He replied that he wasn't. That was how I made use of the servants of others, like a true gentleman.

It was a dark night, and we all returned home. I went in and found the rag-clad soldier with a large wax taper. It had been given to him to carry alongside a dead man and he had walked off with it. This fellow was named Maguso and came from Olías. He had had the role of captain in a play and had battled the Moors in a dancing scene. When he was talking with someone who had fought in Flanders, he would say that he had fought in China; and when chatting with someone just returned from China, that he had served in Flanders. He was always talking about dressing up a line of battle, but the only one he had ever been in was in the fight against fleas. He would speak of famous castles which he had rarely ever seen even engraved on a coin. He warmly praised the memory of Don Juan de Austria and I often heard him say that Luis Quejada [Charles V's steward] had been a loyal friend. He named off Turks, galleons, and captains about which he had read in popular ballads on these subjects. He knew nothing about seafaring — the closest he ever got to the navy was the bean of the same name—. Nevertheless, when he told us about the battle that Don Juan had had at Lepanto, he said that "that Lepanto" certainly was a very brave Moor: the poor chap didn't know that Lepanto was the name of a sea. We surely whiled away some highly amusing moments with him.

My sponsor then came in, his nose flattened out and his head all bandaged with rags, covered with blood and as dirty as could be. We asked him the cause of all this. He replied that he had gone to the soup kitchen at Saint Jerome's and that he had asked for a double portion saying that it was for some poor but worthy people. The monks took the servings from the other beggars' portions to give it to him. The beggars angrily followed him and saw that he was avidly gulping away in a corner behind the door. They began to argue that it wasn't right to deceive to devour and deprive others of their share. As voices rose so did sticks and cudgels and bumps and bruises on my poor friend's head. They clouted him with earthen jars, but the harm done to his nose was caused by a wooden bowl which was given to him to smell a bit faster than usual. They took away his sword. The doorkeeper came out because of the noise, but even he could not quiet them down. Finally my poor sponsor found himself in such danger that he cried: "I'll give up all I've eaten." Even that wasn't enough, because the only thing the beggars could think about was that he had pretended to beg for others and then had hidden to eat his soup.

"Look at that bundle of tatters fit for a ragdoll," said a student with an alms basket in his hand, "sadder than a pastry shop during Lent. There are more holes on him than in a flute, more patches on that outfit than on a dappled mare, and more spots than on jasper or than the dots in a book of music. The men who come for the holy saint's soup could be anybody from bishops on down, but Sir Penniless here is ashamed to eat it! I myself am a Bachelor of Arts from Siguenza." The doorman put himself between them when an old man began shouting that he was a descendent of the famous Captain Gonzalo Fernández de Córdoba and that he still came for his free bowl of soup.

I'll leave the tale at this point for by now my comrade was already out untangling his bones.

Chapter XVI

IN WHICH THE SAME SORT OF THING CONTINUES,
UNTIL THE WHOLE BAND LANDS IN JAIL

In came Merlo Díaz with his belt hung like a necklace with cups and glasses which, with little fear of the Lord, he had stolen by asking for a drink at the wickets of monasteries. But Don Lorenzo del Pedroso outdid him. He came in with a fine cape. He had been at a billiard table and there exchanged the new one for his own which had so little nap on it that it looked freshly shaven. His usual procedure was to take off his cape as if he wanted to get into the game and put it with the others. Then, as though no one wanted to play him a game, he would go back for his cape and take the best one he saw. Then off he would go. He did the same thing at matches for horseshoes and bowling.

All this was nothing to compare with seeing Don Cosme come home. He would come in surrounded by boys with scrofula, canker and leprosy, and all covered with cuts, and some maimed. He had become a faith-healer by using a few signs of the cross and some prayers he had learned from an old woman. He made more money than any of the others, because if the patient who came to be treated had no bulge under his cape, no money clinking in his pocket or no chickens and capons peeping, there was no place for him. He had already laid waste to half the kingdom. He made people believe whatever he wanted to, for a finer craftsman at lying never was born. So good at the art was he that not even unwittingly did he ever speak the truth. He often spoke of the Christ Child. He would go into a house with a thanks-be-to-God and a the-Holy-Spirit-abide-with-you on his lips. He wore on his person all the paraphernalia of hypocrisy: a rosary of robust beads, and, as if wholly by chance, he would let people see underneath his cape a part of a scourge bespattered with blood—from his nose. He made people believe—with a shrug of his shoulders—that his lice were the itching of a hairshirt and that his ravenous hunger was voluntary fasting. He kept tab on temptations. Whenever he named the devil he would say: "God save us and keep us." He kissed the ground as he entered a church; he said he was unworthy. To women he never lifted his eyes, but

skirts he did. With things like this he held such sway over people that they put themselves in his hands. It was like entrusting one's self to the devil, because he was a gambler, and very skillful (in franker terms, he was a cheat). He sometimes took the name of the Lord in vain, in vain. As for women, he had several children, and two caretakers of a saint's chapel pregnant. To put it briefly, those commandments of God that he didn't break, he fractured.

In came Polance making a big noise. He asked for a brown sack, a large cross, a long false beard and a bell. He walked about at night in this getup, saying: "Think ye of death and pray for those souls, etc." In this way he collected a great deal in alms. When he saw a house open, he would walk right in and if no one was there to hinder him, he would steal whatever he found. If someone caught him at it, he would ring his little bell and say in a voice he could make sound very contrite: "Think ye, brothers, etc." I learned from them about all these tricks and unusual ways to steal in a month's time.

Let's return now to the matter of my showing my comrades the rosary. I told them the story and they heartily applauded my trick; the old lady took the rosary to sell it. She went with it from house to house saying it belonged to a poor young woman who was parting with it so she could get something to eat. She had lies and tricks for every occasion. The old girl would weep with every step. She would wring her hands and sigh bitterly. She called everybody son or daughter. She wore—over a shirtwaist, jacket, underclothes, and both a regular and a woolen skirt—a ragged coat of sackcloth that belonged to a hermit friend she had out in the hills near Alcalá. She ruled over the flock, gave us advice and covered up for us. However, as the devil would have it—and he is never idle where his servants are concerned—one day when she went out to sell some sort of clothes and other little things in a house, someone recognized some of his own belongings. He called an officer of the law and they arrested the old woman on me, Mother Lebrusca [or Ivyvine], as she was called. She confessed the whole thing right away and told how we all lived and that we were gentlemen of plunder.

The constable deposited her in the jail and came on to our house. There he found all of us. He had half a dozen cops with him —walking hangmen all—and slapped all our scroungers' Academy in jail where our whole gentlemanly group was obviously in a most perilous plight.

Chapter XVII

IN WHICH IS GIVEN A DESCRIPTION OF THE JAIL AND WHAT HAPPENED IN IT UNTIL THE OLD WOMAN LEFT. AFTER GETTING A FLOGGING, MY COMRADES WERE PUBLICLY DISGRACED AND I WAS RELEASED ON BAIL

When we got there they put shackles on each of us and started to take us down into a dungeon. Seeing where I was headed, I decided to make use of some of the money I had on me and so, taking out a doubloon, I said to the jailer: "Sir, let me speak to you in private." So that he would do so I let him glimpse some coins; when he saw them he took me aside. "I beg you, sir," I said to him, "to take pity on an honest man." I grasped at his hands and as his palms were used to holding dates of that sort, he closed his fist on the money and said: "I'll check up on your illness and if it's not serious, down you'll go to the dungeon." I answered him meekly. He left me outside while my friends were tossed down below.

I'll not even mention how much people laughed at us both in jail and along the streets all because, as they took us on our way tied together and shoved along, some with capes on and others dragging them, it was such a sight to see some of us a patchwork of colors and others a wine both red and white. Whenever the cop tried to get a fast hold on one of us, our clothes were in such tatters all he grabbed onto was bare flesh, and there was nothing to hold on to. Some left the cops with handfuls of shreds of jackets and breeches. When the rope we had been strung together with was taken off, the rags stuck to it like banners.

Finally, at nightfall, I went to sleep in the hall for persons of quality. I was given a cot. It was a sight to see how some of the inmates went to bed fully sheathed without taking off a stitch of what they had worn all day long and how others stripped off in a jiffy every bit they had on. Still others played cards. And finally, when they were all through, the light was put out. We all forgot about our shackles.

The chamber pot was at the head of my bed and at midnight one prisoner after another came over to let loose their prisoners.

When I first heard the noises—thinking it was thunder—I began to cross myself and to pray to Saint Barbara. But once I realized they had quite an odor, I recognized that these weren't thunderclaps of the better breed. There was such a stench that I thought I'd die. Some of the visitors could have filled a room and others an apartment. Finally I was obliged to tell them to move the crockery elsewhere. We had words over whether they would do it or not. I used my position as top man (it's better to be that with one's jailer than with the king of Castile) and I gave one of the men a belt in the face. He got up so fast that he knocked over the pot. The noise woke up the whole congregation. We started belting each other hotly right there in the dark, and the stench was so terrible that everyone got up. The jailer, thinking some of his vassals were getting away, came running up, well armed, and with a troop of his men. He opened up the room, brought a light, and found out what the trouble was. Everyone blamed me. I tried to get out of it by saying that all night long the others hadn't let me shut an eye for opening theirs. The jailer, seeming to think that to keep from being sent to the dungeon I would give him another doubloon, took matters in hand and ordered me to go down below. I decided to give in rather than pilfer my pouch any more. I was taken down below where my friends received me with shouting and joy. I slept that night without cover. The Lord brought forth the dawn, and we came out of the dungeon. We looked one another over and the first thing we were told to do was to clean up and not for the Virgin without blemish—or get a good lashing. I gave six more *reales*. My comrades had nothing to give and consequently were deferred until nightfall.

Down in the dungeon there was a one-eyed fellow, tall, wearing a moustache, sad-faced, and bent over from the whippings he had had. He had on more iron than there is in Biscay, two sets of shackles and a heavy chain. He was called Big Burly. He told that he had been locked up for airing things, so I suspected it was on account of bellows, a flute or a fan. To anyone who asked him if it was because of these things he answered that it wasn't, that it was for things he'd put behind. I supposed he meant for things far in the past. Finally I found out that he was in for sodomy. When the jailer rebuked him for something, he would call him a hangman's flunky and the trustee general of all types of sin. Our inmate had already confessed to his sins, and so perverse was he that we all covered up our hind quarters with collars like the ones mastiffs wear. No one dared break wind for fear of reminding him where our behinds could be found. He had made friends with a fellow named Robledo whom we nicknamed Husky. He said he was imprisoned for being liberal, and I understood that it was with his hands, in picking up whatever he could lay them on. He had been whipped more times than a coach horse, and there wasn't a hangman in the business who hadn't tried his hand on him. His face was badly scarred. He had an odd number of ears and a nose flattened by a direct hit that had split it in two. These two were joined by four other men—as ready for plunder as lions on the prowl—all decked out in fetters and sentenced to forced rowing. They said that soon they would be able to say that they had served the king on both land and sea. It was incredible how happily they looked forward to being shipped out.

All these, peeved to see that my companions had not paid their fee, set out that night to give them a good flogging with a rope designed for that purpose. Night fell. We were herded into a back pocket of the house. The light was put out. Meanwhile I got myself under a bunk. Two of them began to whistle and another to lay it on with the rope. My good gentlemen (who saw the bad turn business had taken) squeezed together their starved carcasses (supped on, eaten and devoured by mange and by lice) so that they all just fit in a crack in the bedstead. They were like nits in the hair or nests of bugs in a bed. The blows rained down on the wood and my companions were silent. When there was no outcry, the other scoundrels left off with the whip and began throwing bricks, stones and other rubbish they had gathered up. Off they flew until one hit Don Toribio in the back of the head and cracked his skull. He began to scream that he was being killed. So his shouts wouldn't be heard, the scoundrels all began to sing and rattle their chains. In hopes of hiding himself, the victim grabbed hold of the others and tried to get underneath. With the effort that was made, all their bones rattled like a beggar's clappers. That was the end of their clothes. Not a rag was left in one piece. The stones and debris came down at such a rate that soon Don Toribio had more cuts in his head than a doublet has slashes. He realized that he was so far on his way to a martyr's death (but not as saintly) that he asked them to let him out, that he would pay them later and give them his clothes as security. It was agreed on. In spite of his companions who had fought in their mutual defense, and all bruised as he was, he got up as well as he could and came over by me. Although the others were quick to agree to do the same thing, their domes were already more heavily roofed with tile than with hair. They offered their clothes too, for they realized that it was better to have to stay in bed because of lack of clothes than because of broken bones. That settled, the ruffians let them be for the night. The next morning they asked my comrades to strip, and when they had done so, it was found that their clothes all together would not make so much as the wick of a candle. The poor souls were wrapped up in a blanket of the kind called a poncho, which is where the delousing is done. They soon began to regret their blanket shelter because one of the fleas there had a ravenous appetite. Some of the fleas were as big as work horses and others could have gone straight for the ear of a bull. My friends feared they would be eaten away that morning, so they got out from under the blanket cursing their luck and half cut into shreds from their furious scratching. I walked out of the dungeon asking their pardon for not keeping them company because, to tell the truth, that was one thing I surely did not want to keep. I greased the jailer's palm with three eight-*real* pieces and since I knew who the notary was who was handling our case, I sent off a little rascal of a boy to get him for me. When he came I took him into another room and began to tell him — after discussing the case — that I had a little money. I begged him to keep it for me and to favor the cause of an unfortunate gentleman who had mistakenly become involved in this affair. "You can be quite sure," he said after swallowing the bait, "that we hold the trumps, and if one of us decides to be dishonest he can do a lot of harm. I have sent more men to the galleys free of charge and out of sheer whim than there are words in a lawsuit. Just trust me and you can be sure I'll get you out of this safe and sound."

He then got up to go, but turned around at the door to ask me for something for good old Diego García, the constable, who had to be kept quiet with a gag made of silver. He also reminded me of something for the court reporter for the costs of doctoring records. He went on, "A court reporter, sir, with an arch of the brow, a rise in the voice, a tap of the foot to get the mayor's attention (when his attention wanders) can start an action that will ruin a man." I got the idea and added another fifty *reales*. As repayment he told me to straighten the collar of my cape and gave me two cures for the cold I had (caught from the chill of the jail). Finally he said to me: "Don't worry, with eight *reales* to the jailer, things will be better. These people show no charity unless they're paid for it." This remark pleased me no end. Finally he left. I gave the jailer an *escudo* and he removed my chains.

He let me come to his home. He had a whale of a wife and two daughters of Satan, ugly and dumb, and a couple of whores in spite of their looks. It so happened that the jailer (whose name was Something-or-other Baldones de San Pablo and whose wife was Doña Ana de Mora) came home to dinner while I was there. He was snorting with anger and didn't want to eat anything. His wife, who saw there was something wrong, went over to him and got him so mad that he blurted out: "What do you think is wrong! That lousy thief Almendros, the landlord, told me when I was talking to him about the lease that you aren't clean."

"Did that scoundrel get that much dirt out of me?" she cried. "By the head of my grandfather, you're certainly no man or you would have snatched him bald. Do I call in his servants to clean me up?"

She turned to me and said: "They can't call me a Jew the way they do him. Of the four quarters he comes from, two are no good and the rest of the cash is all Hebrew. I tell you, Señor Don Pablo, if I had heard him I would have reminded him that he's been made to wear the [Inquisition's] Saint Andrew's cross."

Then the jailer, all excited, answered: "But woman! I kept my mouth shut because he said that the cross you were sewing was a similar kind. When he said dirty he didn't mean like a pig, but because you won't eat any." "So he called me a Jewess? And you can say it so calmly, for heaven's sake? Is that all you care for the honor of Doña Ana de Mora, the granddaughter of Esteban Rubio and daughter of Juan de Madrid, as God and everybody else knows?"

"What do you mean," I asked, "the daughter of Juan de Madrid?"

"Of Juan de Madrid," she replied, "daughter of the one from Auñón."

"I swear to God," I said, "that the scoundrel who said such a thing is a Jew, a fairy and a cuckold, because Juan de Madrid, my lord (may he rest in peace), was my father's first cousin and I'll show proof of who and what he was. This concerns me personally and if I get out of jail, I'll make that scoundrel take back his lies a hundred times over. I have documents in my hometown certifying who they both were in letters of gold."

They were both overjoyed and took heart on hearing about the documents. Of course I had no such thing nor did I even know who they were. The husband wanted to get detailed information on the family relationship. So that he wouldn't catch me in a lie, I acted as if I were half crazy with anger, cursing and swearing. They were concerned for me and said I shouldn't think about it or worry over it any more. Ever so often I let myself make a slip and would say: "Juan de Madrid! We'll see if the evidence I have is a joking matter." Then later on I'd say: "Juan de Madrid, senior, was married to Ana de Acebedo, the fat." Then I'd keep still for a while.

Finally because of all these things the jailer fed me and gave me a bed in his house. The notary — at the jailer's instigation and bribed with my money — arranged things so well that the old lady, riding a brown horse which was led by the bridle and preceeded by a man who sang out her evil doings, was taken out for all to see. The crier called out: "This woman for thievery." The hangman kept time with a whip on her ribs as the magistrates had told him to do. All of my former companions came next, riding along, their heads and faces bare. They were being led out so their shame would be public, but the shreds of clothing left them so bare, it was their privates made public. They were exiled for six years. Through the notary's good graces I got out on bail. The court reporter did his part too because he said a lot in a low, hoarse voice, omitted information and chewed up whole paragraphs.

Chapter XVIII

ABOUT HOW I FOUND LODGINGS AND THE MISHAP
THAT BEFELL ME THERE

I got out of jail. I was alone and without my friends. Although they had told me they were heading for Seville with some help from charity, I did not want to go along with them. I decided to go to a house where they rented rooms, and there I met a young lady, blond and fair, sharp-eyed, bright, obtruding and often intruding, and in heat. She lisped just a bit. She was afraid of mice and was very proud of her hands. So she could show them off she was always snuffing out candles and served up the food at the table; she was always pointing out things. In church she would always fold her hands in front of her. She would walk along the street pointing out the house of first one person and then another. in her own living room she was forever arranging a pin in her hair. If she played any kind of game, it was always "the pinching game" because it gave her the opportunity to show off her hands. She would yawn — on purpose without any real need to do so — just so she could show off her teeth and then use her hands to cover her mouth. To put it briefly, she had handled the household for such a long time that even her parents were tired of it. They received me very cordially in their house because they were interested in their rent. There were three lodgers. I was one; the second was a Portuguese and the other a Catalan. They gave me a hearty welcome. I thought the girl might be good for some fun and recognized how convenient it was to have her right there in the house. I flirted with her. I would tell stories around the house I had got ready to entertain them with. I brought them news, though nothing is new. I did everything for them that didn't cost anything. I told them I knew a great deal about magic, and that I would make the house appear to catch fire and other things which they —as gullible souls — gobbled up. I won their good will through gratitude, though not through love, for I was not as well accoutered as might have been expected — although I was better off than before, thanks to the jailer whom I still visited; that way I kept up our blood relation-

112

ship, with the meat and bread I ate up on him — they were not as nice to me as I felt they should be.

To gain a good reputation I decided to send some friends to the house to ask for me when I was not at home. The first one to come by asked for Don Ramiro de Guzmán, which was the name I used. My friends had told me that it cost nothing to change one's name, and that it was very handy. Thus he asked for Don Ramiro, "a rich business man who has already had two commissions from the king." The two women didn't recognize me from this and answered that the only Don Ramiro de Guzmán who lived there was more wretched than rich, of slight build, ugly face and a poor man. "That's the one," my friend replied, "the same one I'm asking for. I'd never in God's glory want for more income than his which is more than two thousand *ducados*." He told them a few whoppers. They stood there amazed. He left them a false draft for nine thousand *escudos* he had come to get from me; he asked them to see that I got it. Both mother and daughter believed the tales of my wealth and immediately marked me out as a good match. I arrived pretending to know nothing of all this and when I walked in they handed me the draft saying: "Money and love are hard things to hide, Señor Don Ramiro. Why have you hidden your true identity from us as good as we've been to you?" I acted as if I were put out over the note and went up to my room. It was something to witness how, once they thought I had money, they flattered me that everything I did was all right. They revered my every word. Such wit as I had was unique. When I saw they were dying to take the bait, I declared my intentions to the daughter. She listened delightedly, then flattered me no end. We parted company. One night later on, to convince them even more of my wealth, I closed myself in my room, which was separated from theirs by only a thin wall, and took out fifty *escudos*. I counted them over so many times they heard me count to six thousand *escudos*. Seeing that I had so much ready cash, they outdid themselves entertaining and waiting on me.

The Portuguese lodger was called O Senhor Vasco de Meneses, a gentleman of the Order of Christus. He wore a long baize cape, boots, a collar that was small and a moustache that was big. He was dying of love for Doña Berenguela de Rebolledo, which was the young lady's name. He wooed her by sitting and talking with her and by sighing more than a sanctimonious old woman at Lenten service. He sang badly and was always at odds with the Catalan who was the saddest and most wretched creature God ever made. He ate feverishly, every third day, and the bread he consumed was

so hard even a backbiter would have found it too much to chew over. He put on a show of being very manly, but was really quite chicken, except for not laying eggs, as all his cackling made clear. When the two of them saw that I was making progress, they began to say disparaging things about me. The Portuguese said I was lousy, a picaro and worthless. The Catalan called me a despicable coward. I knew all about it and even overheard them sometimes, but I had no desire to answer them back. Finally the young lady began to talk to me and to answer my love notes. I would begin them in the usual way: "This audacity, your great beauty, etc." I offered to be her slave and signed my name with a heart pierced by an arrow. We finally got around to using the familiar *tú* with each other. I went out and rented a mule so as to build up my reputation as a gentleman of quality. Then, all bundled up and disguising my voice, I came back to the house and asked for myself, and if that was the lodging of Señor Don Ramiro de Guzmán, Lord of Valcerrado and Velorete. "A gentleman of that name," the girl replied, "does live here. He's a man of slight build." I said that from her description that was the man and I begged her to tell him that Diego de Solórzano, his sometime treasurer, was out making collections and had come by to pay his respects. After that I went on my way and then came back to the house a little while later. I was welcomed home with the greatest joy in the world. My landladies asked me why I had hidden from them the fact that I was Lord of Valcerrado and Velorete, then gave me the message.

This was too much for the poor girl, she was so greedy for a rich husband. She arranged for me to come to talk with her late one night, telling me to use a hallway that opened out onto the roof, from which I could get to the window of her room. The devil, who always keeps his eyes open, so arranged things that when night came, I, excitedly anticipating the pleasure of the meeting, went up to the passageway. While getting from there to the roof, my feet slipped and I fell over onto the roof of a notary next door with such a maddening blow that I broke all the tiles. On hearing the noise the whole household woke up. As the notary thought it was thieves — men of his profession are very susceptible to thievery — everybody came up to the roof. When I saw what was happening, I tried to hide behind a chimney, but this only increased their suspicion. Consequently the notary and his brother and two servants gave me a severe drubbing and tied me up right before my lady friend's eyes. I could think of nothing to do to stop them. The girl, meanwhile, was having a good laugh because, since I had told her I knew how to do tricks and cast spells, she thought I had fallen in

115

such a fix to be amusing, and through magic. As a result she kept telling me to get up, that that was enough for now. With such goings on and the blows from stick and fist I was getting, I began to howl. She still thought it was all a joke and couldn't stop laughing.

The notary then began to prepare his case against me, and because he heard keys jangle in my pocket, he both declared and wrote down that I had skeleton keys and, although he saw them himself, there was no way to convince him that they were not. I told him my name was Don Ramiro de Guzmán and he had a good laugh over that. I was feeling depressed — here I was all beaten up right before the eyes of my lady friend, about to be arrested without any cause and getting a bad reputation — I didn't know what to do. I got down on my knees, but it was to no avail.

All of this took place out on the roof, for even in full view of heaven men like the notary bear false witness. He gave the order to take me downstairs, and they lowered me through a window into a room that was used as a kitchen.

Chapter XIX

IN WHICH THE SAME STORY CONTINUES, PLUS
SOME OTHER EVENTS

I didn't close my eyes all night long for thinking of what a misfortune it was not only to have fallen on the roof but into the hands
of the notary. When I thought of my skeleton keys and the pages
he had filled writing it all down, I began to realize that nothing
grows at such a phenominal rate as guilt in the hands of a notary.
I spent the night thinking up schemes. I even thought of begging
for mercy in Christ's name, but remembering what He had had to
bear from notaries during His lifetime, I did not dare. Any number
of times I tried to get out of my ropes, but the notary heard me
right away and would get up and tighten the knots. He was wider
awake fabricating his lies than I at trying to get free. He got up
and dressed so early the next morning that everybody in the household except the witnesses were still in bed. He took up a leather strap
and gave my ribs another going over. He gave me a sermon on the
evils of stealing, a subject he was well acquainted with. As this
was going on, he beating me and I about ready to give him a
bribe — which is the blood of the lamb that cuts such hard hearts
to size — the Portuguese and the Catalan walked in. They had been
persuaded to come by the pleas of my ladylove who had seen me
fall and be beaten and who finally realized it was not enchantment
but miserably bad luck. When the notary saw them talking to me,
he took up his pen and wanted to stick them with being accomplices
in the crime. The Portuguese wouldn't put up with this and began
to lecture him, saying that he was a nobleman of the king's household and that I was a *home muito fidalgo,* and that it was a dirty
trick to keep me tied up. He began to undo the knots, but almost
immediately the notary began to shout: "Resisting arrest!" Then
two of his assistants — half constable and half thug — began to
stamp on their capes and to unfasten their collars, as they always
do when they try to act out one of the fights they never really get

into. And they called for the king's help. My two friends finally got me untied. The notary, who saw that no one would help him, said: "I swear to heaven you can't do this to me, and if you weren't who you are, it would cost you plenty. Well, do something for these witnesses and notice that I'm getting nothing for my trouble." I got the idea; I took out eight *reales* and gave them to him. I felt about ready to return the beating he had given me, but in order not to have to admit publicly that I had received one, I left him as he was and went off with my friends, thanking them for my freedom and ransom. I returned home with my face covered with welts and my back the sadder for its unhappy drubbing.

The Catalan had a good laugh over it all and told the girl she should marry me so that she could reverse the old proverb about not going after the cuckold with a whip in her hand, but after the man who'd been whipped with horns in her hand. He said I was despaired and spoiled (by the rod). I was deeply offended by these puns. Whenever I went to visit them, they would start talking about measuring with a yardstick or about kindling or lumber. Once I saw that I had become a laughingstock and that they had caught on to the flowery tale of my wealth, I decided to be on my way. In order not to have to pay for either my board or my room (which had mounted to a considerable sum) and to get my luggage out too, I arranged for a friend of mine named Brandalagus, who was from Hornillos, and two other friends, to come by on a certain night and put me under arrest. They came as we had agreed and informed the landlady that they were members of the Holy Inquisition and that she had better keep things quiet. The women were frightened to death and afraid they'd be sent to prison because of the sorcery I had supposedly practiced while living there. They said not a word as I was led out, but when they saw the luggage being carried away, they asked about their bills. My friends said that everything was being confiscated by the Inquisition. Neither poor soul had any answer to that. They let them by and then stood there saying that they had long been afraid of just such a thing. They told the Catalan and the Portuguese about the men who had come for me and carried me off. They both said they were demons and that I had them in my service. Then they told about the money I had counted. They said that although it seemed to be money at the time, it wasn't at all. They believed every word of it. At least I got my belongings out without paying a cent for my board.

I now decided, with the aid of my friends, to change my way of dress and to wear the newest and most fashionable breeches and an open collar. I knew it was also very stylish to have a servant (or two). My friends urged me on by pointing out the advantages to be gained by being able to make a wealthy match. This sort of thing happened frequently in the capital, they said, and they added that they would steer me to the right spot and would help me with the means to follow through. Feeling very sharp, and greedy to hook a wife, I decided to follow their suggestions.

I went to a number of sales and bought my wedding finery. I found out where horses could be rented and got myself one. The first day I didn't find a servant. I went to the Calle Mayor and stood in front of a harness shop like a person who was going to buy something. Two gentlemen came up, each with two lackeys. They asked me if I was going to buy the silver trappings I had in my hands. I began to talk, and with some courteous remarks, I got the gentlemen to stay with me a while. Finally they said they wanted to go to the Prado for some fun and I said that if they had no objections that I would go along too. I instructed the shopkeeper to send my two pages and my lackey to the Prado if they came by there. I described their livery and then got between the two gentlemen and off we went. I kept thinking that no one seeing us could determine with certainty whose the pages and lackeys were or which one of us had none with him. I began to discuss enthusiastically the equestrian exercises at Talavera and told them about a white horse I had. I sang the praises of a stallion I was waiting to have brought to me from Cordova. Whenever we encountered a page or lackey on horseback, I would have him stop and would inquire whose horse it was. Then I would discuss its good points, and so on, and ask if it was for sale. I would then have it give a couple of turns there in the street and even though nothing was wrong with it I would find some defect in the bridle and then make suggestions for fixing it. As luck would have it, I found several occasions to do this sort of thing. Since my two companions were fascinated and I imagined they were saying to themselves: "Who in the world is this broken-down gentleman?" (one of them was wearing the insignia of a military order on his breast and the other a diamond chain which was both insignia and badge of a knight commander), I said that I was going about trying to find good horses for myself and a cousin of mine as we planned to enter some contests.

When we got to the Prado I dismounted very properly and began to walk around. I had my cape thrown over my shoulder and my hat in my hand. Everybody was looking at me. Someone said: "I've seen him walking around before." Someone else commented: "He's a good-looking devil." I acted as though I hadn't heard a thing and kept on strolling.

My two friends had gone up to a coach with some ladies in it and asked me to join them for a bit of fun. I left the young women to them and went around to the side the mother and aunt were on. They were a couple of merry old gals, one about fifty and the other just a bit younger. I paid them all sorts of compliments and they took it all in, for no matter how old she may be, there's no woman alive whose vanity is not greater than her age. I promised them some presents and asked them the marital status of the two young women. They replied that they were both single, which was obvious from their conversation. I said the usual thing about hoping that they would be provided for in the manner they deserved. They liked the expression "provided for" very much. They went on to ask me what I was doing in the capital. I told them I had come to get away from a father and mother who wanted to marry me against my will to a woman who was ugly and stupid and ill-bred, but with a large dowry. Then I went on: "Ladies, I would rather have a girl of good family come to me without a stitch to her name than marry some Jewess, wealth and all. After all, thanks be to God, my estate is worth almost four thousand *ducades* in income. If I win a lawsuit I have well under way, I'll have no need for anything." The aunt quickly replied: "Oh, sir, how I admire you! Don't you marry unless it's a girl you care for and a woman of good background. I can assure you that even though I'm not very rich, I have refused to marry off my niece to several wealthy suitors because they weren't gentlemen of quality. She may be poor, for she has only six thousand *ducados* dowry, but no one can better her in background and breeding."

"I'm quite sure of that," I said.

At that point the two young ladies brought an end to the conversation by asking my friends to take them to lunch.

They looked at each other and their beards were a-tremble.

Seeing the situation I said that I had need of my pages as there was no one else I could send for some boxes I had at home. They thanked me, and I begged them to go with me to the Casa del Campo the next day. I said I would send along a picnic lunch. They accepted right away. They told me their address and asked me for mine. Then the coach left and my companions and I started for home. They showed quite a fondness for me, seeing how shrewdly I had arranged for the luncheon and, in order to put me under obligation to invite them in turn, insisted that I have supper with them that night. I let myself be urged a bit and then dined with them, sending out now and then in search of my servants and swearing I'd discharge them. At ten o'clock I said that I had a date and asked to be excused. I made my departure after arranging to meet them the next afternoon at the Casa del Campo.

I took my horse back to the man I had rented it from and then went on home. I found my companions having a game of *quínola*. I told them what had happened and what arrangements had been made. We decided to send the luncheon without fail and to expend two hundred *reales* on it. After that we went to bed. I must confess I couldn't sleep the whole night long for mulling over what I could do with that dowry. I couldn't make up my mind whether to buy a house with it or an annuity, not knowing which would be preferable and more profitable to me.

Chapter XX

IN WHICH THE STORY CONTINUES, WITH FURTHER NOTEWORTHY EVENTS AND MISFORTUNES

In the morning we got up and began to make our plans about servants, silver and food. Briefly, since money has come to command such universal respect, I paid the butler of a certain gentleman to use his silver and to do the serving with three other servants. I spent the morning getting everything we needed ready, and by afternoon had gone out to rent my horse. I started out for the Casa del Campo at the time we had agreed on. I had my belt stuffed with what looked like legal papers and left six buttons of my doublet unbuttoned so that some other papers would show. When I got to the appointed place, the ladies and the gentlemen were already there. The ladies greeted me very affectionately and addressed me using the *vos* form to show their friendship for me. I had told them that my name was Don Felipe Tristán and so for the rest of the day it was Don-Felipe-this and Don-Felipe-that. I began to tell them that I had been so involved with business for His Majesty and with some accounts for my estate that I had been afraid I might not be able to keep our appointment and so, for that reason, had had to get the luncheon ready on the spur of the moment. Just then the butler came up with all sorts of equipment, the silver and tables. My friends and the ladies just stood there in silence and stared at me. I ordered the butler to go to the summerhouse and set things up there while we took a stroll down to the reservoirs. The women came up to me to compliment me on everything. I was happy to see the girls with their faces uncovered, for never in all my life did I ever see a prettier little thing than the girl I was set on marrying. She was fair-skinned, blond and had rosy cheeks. Her mouth was small and her teeth tiny and set tightly together. She had a nicely shaped nose, round green eyes, was tall and had lovely hands. The other girl wasn't bad, but she was more forward and made me think she probably liked kissing parties. We walked down and looked at the reservoirs. During the conversation I recognized that my betrothed would have had a dangerous time if she had lived under Herod, because she was so innocent. She didn't know anything. But since I'm not interested in women for their counsel or wit but to go to bed with, and since, if they are ugly and wise, it is like going to bed with Aristotle or Seneca or some book, I pick out the ones that are built for the arts of transgression. As we walked up to the summer-house we passed through a bower where a branch of a tree caught in the edging of my collar and tore it a bit. The girl came over and pinned it up for me with a silver pin. Her mother told me to send the collar to their house the next day and that Doña Ana, which was the girl's name, would mend it for me. Everything turned out beautifully; there was plenty to eat of both hot and cold food, appetizers and dessert.

The luncheon went along gaily; I was gallant with the ladies, and they were gracious to me. While the service was being cleared away I saw a gentleman and two servants approaching through the garden. Lo and behold, I recognized my old friend Don Diego Coronel. He came over to me, and seeing me in that outfit, couldn't stop staring at me. He spoke to the ladies and addressed them as cousins. Through it all he kept turning to stare at me. I was busy talking to the butler. My two friends were having quite a conversation with Don Diego, for they were old friends. He inquired — as I learned later on — what my name was and they replied: "Don Felipe Tristán, a very noble and wealthy gentleman." I saw him make the sign of the cross. Finally, right in front of everyone there, he came over to me and said: "I hope you'll pardon me, but I swear that until I learned your name I took you for someone quite different. I have never seen anyone look so much like a servant I had in Segovia, a fellow named Pablillos who was the son of a barber." Everybody had a good laugh at this and I made an effort not to blush. I said I would certainly like to meet that fellow, because any number of people had told me how closely I resembled him. "Good Lord," said Don Diego, "What do you mean 'resemble'? In build, speech, gestures, why, I've never seen such a thing. I mean, sir, it really is incredible. I've never seen anything like it." With that the aunt and the mother both asked how so fine a gentleman could possibly resemble a rascal as low as that. Then so that no one would have any more suspicions, one of them said: "I know Don Felipe very well for he is the very man who, at the request of my husband who was a great friend of his, received us so hospitably in Ocaña." I got the picture and said that I always had been and always would be completely at their service wherever I might be. Don Diego said he was my servant and begged my pardon for having offended me by taking me for the son of a barber. He went on saying: "You will never believe it, but his mother was a witch, his father a thief, his uncle a hangman and he himself one of the most wretched and disreputable men on God's green earth." Imagine how I felt when I heard such things said about me right in my face!' Even though I tried to hide it, I was burning up. We then talked about coming out to that spot. The two gentlemen and I took our leave and Don Diego got into the coach with the women. He asked them the occasion for the picnic lunch and how they happened to be with me. Both mother and aunt explained that I was heir to a considerable fortune and that I wanted to marry Ana. They told him to find out for himself and he would see it was not just a good match but quite an honor for the whole family. They passed the time talking about all this until they reached their house which was on Arenal Street in the San Felipe section.

My friends and I went home together, as we had the night before. They invited me to play cards in the hope of fleecing me. I understood what they were up to and sat down. They got out some cards — which had been doctored up. I lost the first round, then I began to use a trick I knew and won some three hundred *reales* from them. After that I said goodnight and went home.

I found my friends Brandalagas and Pero López who were working on some new tricks with dice. When they saw me they dropped everything to ask me what had happened. I came in looking mournful and all muffled up. I only told them I had been caught in a tight fix. I related how I had run into Don Diego and what had gone on. They comforted me by advising me to overlook it all and not to give up my courtship for any reason whatsoever.

Just then we learned that a game of lansquenet or *pintas* was going on in a neighboring druggist's shop. I knew the game fairly well. Besides that I had more tricks than a May pole has ribbons and a very nicely marked deck of cards. We made up our minds to go over and make a killing (that's what we call it when we inter a bag of money). I sent my friends on ahead. They went into the room where the game was and asked if those who were playing would like a few hands with a Benedictine friar who had just come to convalesce from an illness in the house of some cousins of theirs and that he had a good bit of cash on him. They all got a glint in their eyes and began shouting.

"Have the friar come over."

"He is a very serious person in his order," Pero López explained, "but since he is out now, he wants to play a little game which he likes more for conversation than anything else.

"Just bring him on in," they shouted, "whatever he likes to play for."

Then Brandalagas said: "No one else should come in, for the looks of the thing . . ."

The host answered: "Don't worry about that."

By then they felt quite sure of their ground and believed the whole tale. When my friends got back as acolytes, I already had a nightcap on my head and was wearing my Benedictine friar's habit, glasses and a beard which was clean looking and helped the disguise. I came in acting very humble and sat down. The game got under way. They started off well for it was a case of three against one. They ended up all three undone because I who knew more than they gave them such a tricking that in some three hours' time I won over thirteen hundred *reales*. I left some tips and with a "praised be the Lord" said goodbye to them, but not before asking them not to be scandalized at seeing me play cards as it was just a bit of entertainment and nothing more. The others, as they had lost every cent they had, said they'd all be damned. I said goodnight, and my friends and I left.

We got home at 1:30 that morning and went to bed after we had divided up the spoils. I felt somewhat consoled over what had happened and so the next morning I got up and went out to get a horse. I couldn't find any for rent, a fact which made me realize that there were many others in my same situation, for it looked bad to be on foot and especially for me that day. I went toward San Felipe and there I ran into a lackey who was holding the horse of a lawyer who had just gone in to hear mass. I slipped four *reales* into his hand and asked him to let me do a couple of turns on horseback down the Calle del Arenal. I rode up and down the street a couple of times without seeing anyone. As I was going up a third time, Doña Ana appeared at her window. When I saw her I wanted to show off a bit — even though I didn't know the peculiarities of that horse and wasn't even a good rider. I gave him a couple of whacks and pulled back on the reins. He reared up and gave a couple of kicks. Then he started to run for all he was worth and tossed me on my ear in a pool of water. When I saw I was in such a state, surrounded by urchins who had come running up and right in front of my ladylove, I began to say: "Oh you sonuvabitch! If only you weren't such a fine horse! I'm going to have to stop taking all these chances. They told me he was tricky, but I insisted on riding him." The lackey had already brought the horse back, for it had stopped right away. I mounted once more, but on hearing the commotion, Don Diego Coronel, who was staying at his cousin's house, came to the window. When I saw him I changed color. He asked me if anything was wrong. I told him there wasn't,

125

even though one of my legs was half broken. The lackey was trying to hurry me so that his master wouldn't come out and see what was going on, for he had to go to the palace. I am so unlucky that while the boy was telling me to get on my way, up comes the lawyer from behind, and recognizing his mount, he starts in on the lackey and begins to give him a good beating, all the time asking at the top of his voice why in the devil he had let anyone ride his horse. The worst of all was that he turned around to me as mad as could be and told me in no uncertain terms to dismount. All of this took place in front of my lady friend and Don Diego. No convict whipped through the streets ever felt so ashamed. I was very downhearted, to see two such misfortunes befall me one after the other. There was nothing else to do but to dismount. The lawyer got on his horse and rode away. Meanwhile, hoping to undo the damage, I stayed there in the street chatting with Don Diego. I said:

"Never in all my life have I been on such a wicked beast. My own blossom-colored horse is back at San Felipe. He's fast in a race and a good trotter. I was telling some people how I made him race and come to a halt. They said they knew one I couldn't handle (the one belonging to the lawyer) and I wanted to give it a try. You can imagine how hard his haunches are and with such a poor saddle it's a wonder I didn't kill myself."

"Indeed it was," said Don Diego, "and you seem to have hurt your leg."

"Yes, I did," I continued, "and I think I had better get my horse and go home."

My young lady was quite satisfied with the explanation and was sorry that I had had a fall. On the other hand Don Diego became very suspicious about what had happened between the lawyer and me, and that was wholly the cause of my undoing, to say nothing of other misfortunes that befell me. First and foremost of these latter took place when I arrived home. I went up to check on the chest in which I kept, inside a valise, all the money left me from my inheritance plus what I had won — except for a hundred *reales* I carried on me — and found that good old Brandalagas and Pero López had carried it off and were nowhere to be found. I was struck dumb and wondered what in the world I could do to remedy the situation. I said to myself: "Cursed be the man who depends on ill-gotten gains, because it's easy come and easy go. Poor me! What am I going to do?" I didn't know whether I should go after them or call in the police. I decided against the latter because I knew if the police caught them, they would certainly tell about the friar's outfit and a few other of my doings which would mean my ending up on the gallows. And as for going after them, I didn't know where to start.

I finally decided to stay put so that I wouldn't lose out on the marriage as well — for I already saw my losses recouped with the dowry — and to press things forward with all speed. That afternoon after lunch I rented a horse and rode off to my lady friend's street. Since I had no lackey with me and so as not to pass by without one, I stopped to wait at the corner until some man who looked like one came by. Then I would follow along behind him thus getting myself a lackey without really having one. Once I got to the other end of the street, I would get out of sight until another man looking like a lackey went by.

Well, I don't know if it was so apparent that I was the same wretch Don Diego suspected me to be, whether it was because of what he deduced from the episode of the horse and the lackey of the lawyer, or just what caused him to spy on me to try to find out who I was and my source of livelihood. At any rate, he was so diligent about it that he learned the truth in a most extraordinary way. It came about because I kept pressing to get the final marriage papers signed. In his search for information about me, Don Diego, who was being urged on by the women who wanted matters settled, ran across Flechilla the lawyer — who was the one that had invited me to dine when I was living with the noble gentlemen. He was offended that I had never come to see him again and so, when he learned during his conversation with Don Diego that I had been the latter's servant, he informed him about the way I had acted with him. He went on to say that not two days before he had seen me riding very proudly on horseback and that I had told him I was about to make a very rich marriage. Don Diego hesitated no longer. On his way home near the Puerta del Sol he met my two friends, the gentlemen with the insignia and chain, and related to them what was happening. He told them to get themselves ready, and that night when they saw me in the street, to raise a few knots on my head; they would recognize me by his own cape which I would be wearing. They agreed to do it, and as they were going down the street they ran into me. All three of them feigned such pleasure at seeing me that I would have thought we had never been better friends than we were then. We discussed what we might do for entertainment until nightfall. Finally my two friends took their leave and started down the street; Don Diego and I were left alone and started towards San Felipe. As we got near La Paz Street Don Diego said:

127

"By the life of Don Felipe, let's exchange capes. It's important for me to go by here without being recognized.

"Gladly," said I. In all innocence I took his cape and gave him mine. I offered myself to protect him from the rear, but he — having already laid plans to imperil mine — said that it was important for him to go alone and that I should move on. Wearing his cape, I had hardly walked away from him when, as the devil would have it, two men who were lying in wait for him to give him a beating at some little woman's request and who supposed from the cape that I was Don Diego, began to shower me with blows on the back and shoulders. I began to shout, and from my voice and a look at my face they saw that they had the wrong man. They fled and left me there alone in the street with my bruises. I tried to hide the three or four big bumps I had and I stood there for a while, too afraid to set foot in the next street. Finally at midnight, which was the time I usually went to talk with my girl friend, as I came abreast of the entrance to the house, one of Don Diego's friends who was waiting for me makes connection with his club and gives me two blows on the legs and knocks me down. The other one comes up and gives me a cropping from one ear to the other. Then they take my cape and leave me lying there, saying: "That's what a lying, low-born rascal like you has coming." I began to shout and to call for confession. I didn't know what it really was all about, although I suspected from what the men had said that it might be the doings of the landlord whose place I got out of with the trick about the Inquisition, or of the jailer I had defrauded, or even of my companions who had run away. In short, I had so many slashes coming to me that I couldn't tell from which direction they had proceeded (but I never did suspect Don Diego or the real reasons for it all). I kept on calling: "Cape-snatchers!" Hearing me yell, the police came. They propped me up and seeing that I had on my face a gash the length of a hand and was wearing no cape, and not knowing how it had happened, they picked me up and took me off for treatment. They took me to a barber-surgeon who treated me. They asked me where I lived and took me home.

I was put to bed and lay there all night bewildered and pensive, with my face split in two and my legs so badly injured from the blows that I coldn't stand on them. There I was, badly hurt, robbed and in such a fix that I could neither go after my former friends nor do anything about the marriage, neither stay in the capital nor leave it.

128

CHAPTER XXI

CONCERNING MY RECOVERY AND OTHER
SINGULAR MATTERS

The next morning when I awakened, there at the head of my bed was the landlady, an old dame of some years (her score: fifty-five), with her oversized rosary and her face so furrowed it looked like a cauliflower ear or the shell of a walnut. She had quite a reputation in the vicinity, and anyone could sleep with her who wanted to quench his desires. She was called Mary the Guide, for she ran her own house and was procuress for several others. Her place was never empty the whole year long. It was an experience to see the way she instructed young girls how to veil their faces and taught them just what features they should capitalize on. She advised girls with pretty teeth to keep smiling even when they had reason for grief. She instructed those with fine hands as if they were fencers. She showed those with blond hair how to give a toss to the head and let the curls peek out from a mantilla or bonnet. For those with attractive eyes, she advocated making them do pretty little dances, half closing them to make them look sultry, or rolling them upwards. She was so excellent in matters of makeup that swarthy old crows would come to her and she would make them up so skillfully that when they got home their husbands hardly would recognize them they were so fair. Her greatest talent, however, was in making virgins of girls who weren't. I saw her practice all these arts during my week's stay at her house, and (to top it all off) how she taught her girls to get money out of the men, and just what flatteries to use on them. Then she would advise them how to provide a fit setting for the jewel, young girls by means of charm and wit, more mature ones by indebtedness for past favors, and elder women by respect and obligation. She instructed them in the arts of wheedling hard cash and other ways to coax for chains and necklaces. Then she would quote La Vidaña, her counterpart in Alcalá, and La Planosa, from Burgos, both of whom were virtuosos in the art of cheating. I have portrayed all this so that you, seeing into whose hands I had fallen, will take pity on me, and so that you will meditate more attentively on the things she told me. She began with the following words — she always talked in proverbs—: "Don Felipe, my boy, if you keep on rifling the till, the cash drawer will soon be empty. Like father, like son. As the twig bends, so grows the tree. I don't know you or understand your way of life. You're such a boy yet that it wouldn't surprise me if you had a few escapades without realizing that even while we sleep we move closer to the grave. I'm just a mound of mortal clay myself, so I know what I'm talking about. What is all this I hear about you, that you squandered quite a fortune without knowing how or why, and that you were seen, here, acting like a student, there, like a low-down rascal, and still another, like an elegent gentleman, all according to company you were in? Tell me your friends and I'll tell you who you are. Birds of a feather flock together. Remember my lad, there's many a slip twixt the cup and the lip. Go on with you, you little devil, if women have been bothering you, you know very well that I'm the perennial superintendent of that kind of merchandise in this area. Don't run around any more with riffraff, first after one painted-up cutie and then some sly little wench who lifts her skirts to anybody who puts cash in her purse. I give you my word you would have saved many a penny if you had entrusted things to me, because I'm surely not a miser. I swear by the men folk I've laid away (who'll see to it I end up my days in good style) I wouldn't ask for the rent you owe me right now if it weren't that I need a few candles and herbs." She dealt in drugs without being a druggist, and if someone greased her palm, she would slip through the chimney for a night's work.

Once she had ended her monologue and sermon with a request — that was the subject matter she ended up with, but she had had it in mind from the very beginning — I took no fright at her visitation. She had never before been to my room in all the time I had lodged there, except for the day she came in to explain something to me about sorcery and that the police wanted to arrest her. She had concealed her address. She had come up to set me right and to tell me it was another woman named Guide. It's no wonder that with such guides around we all get off on the wrong track. I counted out her money, and while I was doing so, bad luck, which never forgets me, and the devil who remembers me well, conspired to have the police come to arrest my landlady for living in sin. They even knew that her gentleman friend was also in the house. They came into my room. When they saw me in bed and her there beside me, they both let go and raised five or six good-sized welts on me. Then they dragged me out on the floor. Two others had seized my landlady and were calling her a madam and a witch. Who ever would

130

think such a thing of a woman who had led so exemplary a life! When he heard the shouts of the officer and my moaning, the gentleman friend, who was a fruit peddler and was in a room beyond mine, began to make a run for it. When the police saw him and learned the truth — from what another lodger told them — they started out after the culprit and caught him. They left me behind, snatched half bald and badly beaten. But in spite of all my woes, I had to laugh at the remarks those devils made to the Guide. One of them looked straight at her and said: "How becoming a mitre will look on you, Mother! And what a joy it will be to see three thousand turnips dedicated to your service!" Another one of them said: "The lord mayors have already picked out some fine feathers for you so you'll go to jail in style." Finally they came back with the wretch of a man and bound him and the landlady together. They made excuses to me and then left me to myself.

I felt somewhat relieved to see my good old landlady in the condition she was in. Thus the only worry I had was to get on my feet again soon enough to go throw my orange at her. I had my doubts, however — relying on what I was told by a servant who had stayed behind in the house — that she could be kept in prison, because I heard rumors about her being able to fly and other things which did not sound reassuring. I stayed on in the house convalescing for a week and was hardly able to move. The doctor took twelve stitches in my face and I had to use crutches.

I hadn't a cent left, for the hundred *reales* were soon used up on cure, food and lodging. Therefore, since I had no ready cash and wanted to avoid any further expense, I made up my mind to leave the house on crutches and to sell my outfit, some collars and some doublets, all of which were in good condition. Once I had done this, I bought, with the money I had received, an old leather jacket and a doublet of oakum. I put them on with my shabby great-coat which was patched and too large for me, my leggings and over-sized shoes, and turned up the hood of the coat over my head. I wore a bronze Christ hanging around my neck and a rosary. A beggar who was well-schooled in his art taught me, by the tone of my voice and some doleful expressions, how to beg. Thus I began to go through the streets practicing the profession of mendicancy. I sewed up in my doublet the seventy *reales* I had left over. Then I embarked on my alms-gathering, placing my trust in the glibness of my tongue. For a whole week I roamed through the streets crying out in a doleful voice and a wail of supplication: "Alms, good Christian. Servant of the Lord, alms for a poor lame cripple. Have pity on my neediness." This was the patter I used on work days, but on

131

holidays I would start in another tone and say: "Good Christians and the Lord's faithful, for love of that most sublime princess, the Queen of the Angels, the Mother of God, a little charity for a poor soul smitten lame by the hand of the Lord." Then I would pause ever so little, a very important touch, before going on. "Once while I was working in a vineyard, an ill wind, in the brief space of an hour, crippled my limbs. Until then I was well and fit, and since then, just as you see me, praised be the Lord."

With such a spiel the coins came tumbling in and I earned quite a sum. I would have earned even more if it hadn't been for a fellow with a misshappen face who had no arms and only one leg and who made the rounds of the same streets I did, pushing himself on a little cart. He took in more money than I, even though he was less inventive. He would start out in a rasping voice that would end up in a squeak: "Oh servants of Christ, just look how the Lord has punished my sins. Alms for the poor is an offering to God." Then he would add: "In the name of our beloved JeeSOO." He was earning a fortune. I took note, dropped the "s" and said no more than JeeSOO. That inspired more piety. The fact is I changed my patter and raked in the chips.

I had both legs bound up in leather pouches and used my crutches. I slept in the entranceway to a surgeon's house which I shared with a beggar from the same town. He was one of the worst scoundrels God ever created. He was as wealthy as could be and was a sort of dean to us beggars. He took in more than all the rest of us. He had a huge hernia and he tied up his arms in such a way that one looked crippled and red with infection and the other one missing. He would stretch out full length on the ground at his accustomed place in such a way that the hernia looked as large as a bowling ball and then he would say: "Have pity on my poverty and the burden the Lord has sent on a poor Christian soul!" If a woman went by he would say: "Lovely lady, may God touch your heart." A number of people gave him alms and even went out of their way to do so because he flattered them so. If a common soldier walked by, he would address him as: "Oh, Captain sir!" or if a plain, ordinary man was going by, he would stop him with an "Oh most worthy gentleman!" For those who rode by in a coach, he would address them as lords and ladies, or excellencies. If a clergyman rode by on his mule, he hailed him as "archdeacon." To come right to the point, he fawned something terrible. On people's saint's days, he had still other ways of addressing them. I became such a good friend of his that he told me a secret that could make a man rich in no time at all. My beggar friend had an agreement with three little boys who begged in the streets and stole whatever they could. What they collected they turned over to him for safekeeping. He also had a share in the pilferage of two boys who roamed about with a poor-box.

I decided to follow his example, and he sent people my way on purpose. In less than a month's time I had accumulated more than two hundred *reales*. To crown it all he divulged to me — with the understanding that we would work together — his most valuable secret and the most ingenious undertaking that any mendicant ever devised. We both participated. What we did was: between the two of us, we would carry off four or five small children. When the loss was announced publicly, we would come up to ask for a description of the child. Then we would say: "Yes indeed, sir, I found him at such-and-such a time, and if I hadn't reached him just in time, a cart would surely have run over him. He's safe at my house." The parents would then give us a reward. Soon we had collected so much money with this trick that I had a sum of fifty *escudos,* and my legs had healed, although I still had them wrapped in bandages.

I was determined to leave the capital and to go to Toledo, where I knew no one and no one knew me. I bought myself a brown outfit, a broad collar and a sword. I said goodbye to Baltasar — which was my beggar friend's name — and set out from one inn to another on the way to Toledo.

Chapter XXII

IN WHICH I BECOME AN ACTOR, A POET AND A WOOER OF NUNS, WHOSE QUALITIES ARE NICELY DESCRIBED

In one of the inns I met a company of actors on their way to Toledo. They were traveling in three wagons, and as God would have it, one member of the troupe had been a friend of mine during my student days at Alcalá. He had left the academic life and become an actor. I told him how important it was to me to leave the capital and to go to Toledo. He hardly knew me with the scar on my face and kept crossing himself as he stared at my *per signum crucis*. Finally he befriended me — because of my money — and obtained permission from the others for me to take my place among them. Men and women traveled all jumbled together. One of the women (a dancer who also played queens and other serious roles in their performances), looked like an unusual little wench to me. By chance her husband was sitting beside me. Without being aware of the man's identity and carried away with amorous and passionate desires, I said to him: "Please, sir, tell me how I can get to talk with that woman. I'd glady pay out some twenty or thirty *escudos* on her, she's that pretty to me!" The good man said to me: "It's hardly right for me to go into that subject, for I happen to be her husband. But speaking without passion (for you'll find I feel none), any amount spent on her is money well spent, for such a playful little tidbit of flesh is nowhere else to be found." No sooner had he said this than he leapt down off the wagon and went over to another, to give me the chance to talk with his wife, it would seem. I thought the man's reply had been very astute. It was obvious from men like this that it could be said that they have wives but live as if they had none, to twist the old maxim to worldly purposes. I took advantage of the situation. I spoke to the young lady, and she asked me where I was headed and something about my circumstances and my life. Finally after a long conversation, we arranged a rendezvous for Toledo.

After that, we passed the time of day chattering idly. By chance I began to recite part of a play about Saint Alexis which I remembered from childhood. I played the role so well that I made some of the troupe jealous. My friend in the company, who knew from what I had told him about my misfortunes and reverses, asked me if I would like to throw in my lot with them. The life of traveling players seemed such a fine one that I decided, partly from sheer necessity and partly from interest in the girl, to make a two-year agreement with the director. I signed the contract with him and was given my expense money and my scripts. Just about then we arrived in Toledo.

I was given three or four short plays to study and was assigned some old gentlemen's parts as my voice seemed particularly suited to them. I took great pains with my role and was in the first short play presented there. It was set on a ship—as all of them are—that had been damaged and was without provisions. I had a speech about: "Here is the port." Then before I finished I addressed the audience as "Senate," asked for tolerance of the play's shortcomings and silence during the performance, and made my exit. I got some applause and thus knew I would get along in the theatre.

We gave a performance of a play written by one of our own actors. I was very much surprised to learn that dramatists are found among actors, for I had always thought they were intelligent and well-educated men and not people with so little culture. The truth is that nowadays every producer writes plays, and every actor composes his farce about Moors and Christians. How well I remember the days when, if there was no play by Lope de Vega or Alonso Ramón available, nothing else was to be had. To put it briefly, the first day the play was presented, no one understood a word of it. On the second day, we gave it again. As God would have it, it opened with a war. I came on stage wearing armor and carrying a shield; if I hadn't, I would have been finished off like the others with a bombardment of quinces, stalks, melons and cucumbers. You've never seen such a commotion in all your life. The play deserved it. It was about a king of Normandy who was dressed as a hermit, all with no apparent purpose or design. With him were two lackeys who were supposed to be comedians. To wind up the plot, there was no other way out than to marry everybody off, and that was that. When you consider it, we got what we deserved there on the stage. Afterwards, we all gave our friend the playwright a very hard time. I, for one, told him to consider himself lucky to have made his escape and advised him to profit from his errors. He then swore to God that the play wasn't really his at all, but that by taking one act from one play and a second from another, he had patched it all together like some beggar's cloak. In his opinion the only defect was that some of the seams showed. He

135

did confess to me that the fools who wrote plays were prompted by profit and that they availed themselves of any play they had seen performed, which was easier than writing their own. He added that the three or four hundred *reales* to be earned were well worth the risks. Furthermore, while they were traveling about, authors frequently would bring in unperformed plays for consideration. He said: "We producers take new plays to look at and then steal them for ourselves. By adding some silly bit here and taking out a good passage there, we claim it as our own." He even assured me that no dramatist had ever really known how to compose a couplet otherwise. The scheme didn't sound bad to me.

I must confess that I was taken with the idea, for I had a natural inclination towards poetry, and even more so since I was already somewhat acquainted with several poets. You see I had read Garcilaso. Consequently, I determined to try my skill in the art. With this new activity plus the actress and the performances, my time was well taken up. Within the month's time that we had been in Toledo giving many a good performance, and thus remedying our past mistake, I had acquired a name, for the audience had begun to call me Alonsete, as I had said my name was Alonso. They also called me "The Cruel" because of a role I had played that had been wildy applauded by gentlemen and common herd alike. I now earned three outfits and there were several producers who wanted to entice me away from the troupe. I talked knowingly about theatre, scoffed at the famous, criticized the extravagant posturings of Pinedo, cast my vote for the natural ease of Sanchez and said that Morales did a good job. I was consulted on questions of scenery, settings and equipment. If anyone brought a new play in to be read, I was the one who heard it.

In short, encouraged by the applause I had received, I embarked on my maiden venture as a dramatist-poet with a ballad. After that I wrote a short play which wasn't bad. I even undertook to write a full-length play and just so it couldn't help be other than divine, I wrote it on the subject of Our Lady of the Rosary. It began with music on the flageolets. There were souls in Purgatory and their demons, which were in style then. The townspeople were delighted when I used the name of Satan in my verses and argued whether he had fallen from heaven, and that sort of thing.

In a word, the play was produced and was a success. From then on I had my hands full of work, considering the lovesick suitors who came to me, first one for a verse on eyebrows, then another for one on eyes; the next would ask for one on hands; still another, a ballad on hair. I had a price for each type although I let some

137

go at a bargain so the customers would come to me rather than to my competitors. Talk about carols! I was swamped by orders from sextons and wooers of nuns. Blind men practically supported me with prayers—eight *reales* apiece—, and I recall that at that time I wrote one about the Just Judge, solemn and impressive, which excited most people to charity. I even wrote one for a blind man, who recited it as his own work, and that became well-known and begins as follows:

> Mother of the Human Word,
> Daughter of the King Divine,
> Give me grace of purest kind, etc.

I was the first one to introduce the idea of ending hymns, like sermons, with a "grace in this world and glory in the next," as in this verse about a captive from Tetuan:

> To that high King that hath no dross,
> With heart unsullied let us pray.
> May He our faith view from His cross,
> Grace in this world our lot this day,
> Glory in the next our pay. Amen.

I had clear sailing with such products as this; I was well-off and prosperous and had aspirations of becoming a producer myself. I had my house quite elegantly furnished, for—in order to have some inexpensive coverings—I had gotten into a devilish business, namely the buying in taverns of small tapestries with coats-of-arms on them to hang on the walls. They cost me between twenty-five and thirty *reales;* but they were something to behold, even more so than the king's, though his are a sight to be seen, for mine are hole-ly open to view.

One day an extraordinary thing happened to me and, although humiliating to me, I'll tell it anyway. I had retired to an upstairs room in my house one day that I was working on a play. There I stayed and there I ate. A servant girl would come up with food and leave it there for me. It was my habit to act out a role I was writing as if I were acting it on the stage. As the devil would have it, just at the time the girl was coming up the stairs—which were narrow and dark—carrying two dishes and a pot of stew, I was busily working on a scene about a hunting party. As I was writing my play, I was shouting and recited:

> Hold back the bear! Hold back the bear!
> For me in pieces he doth tear,
> and after thee starts down the stair.

138

What did the girl—who was from a little country town in the north—think when she heard "and after thee starts down the stair"? She thought what was happening was true and that I was shouting a warning. She turns to run and in her confusion, steps on her skirt and goes rolling all the way down the stairs. She spills the stew and breaks all the plates and flies screaming into the streets, yelling that a bear was killing a man. I hurried down after her right away, but the whole neighborhood had already gathered round and was asking about the bear. Even though I explained to them that it was all nonsense on the girl's part—because it was all a part of the dialogue in my play—they still wouldn't believe it. I got nothing to eat that day. My companions heard the tale and it was repeated from one end of town to the other. Many things of a similar sort happened to me while I continued in the profession of dramatist and I could not stay out of trouble. Finally it turned out that our director—they always end up the same way—, when it was learned that things had gone well for him in Toledo, was put in jail for some sort of debt. As a consequence the company broke up, and we each decided to go our separate ways. To tell the truth, although my companions wanted me to direct other troupes, I had no ambitions for such a responsible post. I had begun work in the theatre through sheer necessity, and finding myself solvent and feeling secure, I had just one goal in mind, to have a good time.

I said goodbye to my friends and they left. I, who thought that the end of my troubled ways would coincide with my leaving the artificial life of the actor, if you're not too disgusted with me to read on, became a suitor at the grating, in the manner of the cowl. To put it frankly, I turned into a candidate of the Antichrist, which is to say, a wooer of nuns. I happened to get into this situation because a nun, at whose request I had written a number of carols, took to me during a performance of a Corpus play in which I performed the role of St. John the Evangelist, to whose order she belonged. She showered me with favors and told me that the only thing that upset her was my being an actor—for I had pretended that I was the son of an important nobleman—and on that point she was full of pity for me. Finally I decided to write to her as follows:

LETTER

"More in order to do something pleasing to you, dear lady, than to satisfy myself, I have withdrawn from the actor's company. Indeed all company without yours is solitude for me. Now I shall be all the more yours for being that much more myself. Do not fail to let me know when there will be visiting hours and thus I shall know when my happiness shall begin, etc."

A convent messenger took her the letter. It was incredible how great was the nun's joy when she learned of my new way of life. She wrote me the following answer:

REPLY

"I prefer to withhold my best wishes on the recent happenings in your life until I can convey them personally. I should greatly regret this were I not aware that my good will and your advantage are one and the same. We might say that you have found yourself again. All that is needed now is a perseverance I too shall show. I'm afraid there are no visiting hours today, but do not fail to come at vespers. We shall see each other then and talk with our eyes. I may be able to pull some trick on the abbess. And so, farewell."

The letter made me very happy, for the nun had a good mind and was quite pretty. I ate my dinner and then dressed up in the outfit I had worn when I played leading man on the stage. After that I went to the church, said some prayers, and then began to examine every hole and opening in the grating to see if she had shown up. At last, as God willed in His good hour—it was more like the devil in an evil hour—I heard the signal which was a cough. She began to cough and I began to cough, and soon there was such a devil of a hubbub that you would have thought someone had thrown pepper all over the church. At length I was getting tired of coughing when an old crone who was coughing appeared at the grating. Then I saw my bad luck, for coughing is a dangerous signal to use in a convent. What is a signal to a young woman is a habit in the old, and what sounds like the song of a nightingale is really the cackling of a crow. I stayed there quite a while, until vespers began. I remained to hear them through. That is why nuns' suitors are labeled solemn lovers, because they, like vespers too, are solemn. They never leave vespers happy, so despondent are they that their day never comes. You wouldn't believe the number of vespers I listened to. My neck was a couple of feet longer than when I began wooing, just from stretching it to see what was going on. I became a friend of the sexton and the acolyte and was cordially received by the vicar who was a funny sort of man. He walked about so stiffly that he looked as though he breakfasted on roasting spits and lunched on arrow shafts.

I went to the visitors' windows and found that—although the courtyard was fairly large—one needed to get a spot reserved before twelve o'clock, just as one did for a new hit play. The place was seething with the devout. I finally got in as best I could. It was quite a sight to see the different postures the wooers assumed. Some stood staring without batting an eye. Others, with one hand on their sword and the other on their rosary, looked like marble statues on a tomb. One, with hands raised and arms extended, hovered like an angel receiving the thorns. His neighbor, with his mouth open wider than any demanding woman's and without uttering a word, was baring his very heart to his ladylove, by way of his gullet. Still another, pressed tightly against the wall and a heavy burden to the bricks, appeared to be measuring himself against the corner. Another strode back and forth as if to be admired for his gait, just like a he-mule. Another, holding a love note high in his hand, had the look of a hunter beckoning to his falcon. The jealous lovers made up another group. Some of them gathered in clusters laughing and looking at the girls while others intoned verses and waved them about. Some, to make a ladylove jealous, would stroll in front of the building with another woman by the hand, or would talk to a servant who was in on the plot and would give him a note supposedly from another woman. All this went on down below in our part, but what went on up above where the nuns were was also a sight to behold. The visits took place at a little tower full of cracks and a wall with so much filigree that at first it looked like a sand-blotting shaker or a pomander box. Every hole had its peeper. At one you could see a regular potpourri, here a hand and there a foot; at another, you saw the ingredients for a Saturday's stew, heads and tongues, but nary a brain. One side was like a peddler's stall: one nun would display her rosary and another would finger her handkerchief. In another section a glove would appear or a green ribbon flutter. Some spoke in a loud voice; others coughed. Another would call with a lisp (as hat sellers do), their beckoning fingers like spiders on the webbing of the wall.

It is something to see how in summertime they would not only warm themselves in the sun, but even get themselves scorched. It's an amusing sight to see the women medium-rare and the men well-done. With the humidity in wintertime, some of us sprouted watercress and thickets on our flesh. There is neither any snow that just goes its way, nor any rain that passes us by. In the final analysis all this is just to see a woman through grating and glass as if she were the relic of a saint. It is like falling in love with a thrush in a cage, if your ladyfriend talks; and if she is silent, like wooing a portrait. Their favors are all trial shots that never really make a hit, a bit of a tap with the fingers. They stuff their heads between the grillwork and aim their endearments through the loopholes. They love at hide and seek. They speak in a soft, prayerful voice, and what a sight it is to see them meekly submit to the scoldings of an old woman, a bossy superintendent or a lying gate-keeper! Best of all is the way they show their jealousy of the outside world, protesting that their love is the true one and giving one damned reason after the other to prove it all! I ended up calling the abbess "madam," the vicar "father" and the sexton "brother," all of which with time and events happens to a man who was as far gone as I. The gatekeepers began to bother me with their sending me away, and the nuns with their numerous requests. I began to mull over how expensive was the cost of that hell which for some is so cheap and which in this life takes us down such well-worn pathways. I realized that I was traveling to hell on nothing more than my fine sense of touch. If I carried on a conversation, I usually—so that the others who were there at the grating would not hear me—put my head so close to my nun's that for two days I would have the ironwork's pattern stamped on my brow, and I would talk like a priest saying the words of the consecration. Everybody I ran into would say: "Damn you for a low-down lover of nuns," and other things worse.

All of this got me to thinking things over and I just about made up my mind to give up my nun even though it cost me my sustenance. I made my decision on Saint John the Evangelist's day because I finally learned what nuns are really like. All you need to know, sir, is that the Baptist sisters got hoarse on purpose and, instead of singing the mass, they moaned it. They never washed their faces and they dressed in old rags. The devotees of the Baptist sisters, just to discredit the festivities, brought stools to church instead of chairs, and a whole flock of rascals from the worst part of town.

When I considered how some in the name of one saint and some in the name of another gave their devotees a bad time, I inveigled from my nun, with the explanation I would raffle them off, fifty *escudos* worth of needlework, stockings of silk and pouches full of amber and sweets. Then I set out for Seville. I was afraid if I waited any longer I would see mandrakes being born in the monastery. What the nun's feelings may have been, more for what I took from her than for myself, the pious reader can conjecture.

CONCERNING WHAT HAPPENED TO ME IN SEVILLE UNTIL I EMBARKED FOR THE INDIES

My trip from Toledo to Seville was a prosperous one for I was no novice at gambling and tricks. I carried with me some dice that were loaded; a new crust had altered the face. My right hand was one-die pregnant (for if four turned up, it hatched out three). I carried with me a supply of drawing paper, both large and small, with which to make up an extra trump card or two. That way no cash got away. I won't go into the other tricks I blossomed out with, for if I tried to describe all of them, you'd think I was more a bouquet than a man. Furthermore, the real thing is a far better deal than the counterfeit, as is the describing of such evils so that men may avoid them. Perhaps if I explain some of the tricks and the terms gamblers use, the ignorant will heed my instructions and those who read my book will profit from others' misfortunes.

Don't be overly confident, my friend, just because you're dealing the cards, for they can be switched at a flicker of a candle. Be careful of cards whose corners have been pared down or whose edges have been polished, for both are ways of determining the odds. And just in case you are a scullery boy, reader, I can tell you that in kitchen and stable, cards are marked by a pin prick or by bending them a certain way. If you are dealing with honest folk, watch out for the card that in the printing press was conceived in sin and which, with a line or so across the back, gives the future away. Don't even trust a clean card, for the man who gives a quick glance and remembers what he sponged off is dirty too. Watch out when you play lansquenet, for the man who, when he shuffles, bends the face of the cards, with the exception of the kings, more than the others; the toll he exacts marks the end of your cash. On the first draw, be careful that the dealer doesn't give you off the top what was just discarded and see to it that your opponents don't ask for new cards either with their fingers on the deck or by the first letters of their words. I won't bring any more tricks to light. This should be enough to show you that you have to live prudently, for one thing is certain and that is that there is an infinite number of tricks

I've not even mentioned. *To make a kill* means to win money plus property; *intricacy* is what the trick against a friend is called, and the reason is that it is so intricate not even the friend catches on; *two-faced* is the name for men who carry around coins just waiting for some purse-butcher to try to fleece them; *white* is what the person who is free from guile and as good as fresh bread is called; and *black* is the name for the player who vents his zeal on the white of the bull's eye.

With my jargon and my tricks, I finally arrived in Seville. I won enough money from some cronies to rent a mule and enough from innkeepers on the way to get my food and lodging. I went to stop in an inn called the Moor. There I ran into a former schoolmate of mine from Alcalá, a fellow named Mata who had changed his name—it wasn't resounding enough for him—to Matorral. He dealt in lives and was a merchant of slashes which fit him very well. He carried his advertising on his face; from the ones that had been given him, his customer could bargain over the size and depth of the slash my friend was to give. He would always say: "There is no teacher like the man who has been cut up himself." He was right too, for his face was a leather jacket and he himself no more than one big piece of leather. He invited me to go have some dinner with him and some of his friends and said they would get me back safely to my lodging.

I went with him. When we got to his inn he said: "Hey, take off that there cape and act like a man. Tonight you're going to meet the finest guys in all Seville. Just so they won't think yur a fairy, turn down yur collar and slump over a bit. Let yur cloak drag (we're always dragging around); screw up yur snout, and gesture right and left. When you talk, pronounce yur g's like h's and yur h's like g's. Say this after me: *gerido, mogino, gumo, paheria, mohar, habali* and *harro de vino*. Learn it by heart." He lent me a dagger that was so broad it was like a cutlass and so long that it was not called a sword only through his moderation. "Drink up this half-gallon jug of wine," he said to me. "If you don't have a drink on yur breath, people will think yur not a he-man." While we were talking and I was beginning to feel giddy from the jugful I had drunk, four of the comrades came in, their faces like shoes for the gouty, and weaving from side to side. Instead of wearing their capes in the usual manner, they had them wrapped like skirts around their middles. Their hats were pushed back on their heads and the brims turned up so that they looked like diadems. They were decked out with enough daggers and swords to fill two whole ironworks, the scabbards hanging down to their right heels. Their eyes were

144

half closed, but their glance was piercing. Their moustaches were waxed up like horns, and their beards were like Turks' and as bushy as a horse's tail. They made a sign of greeting with their lips and then said to my friend—their voices were peevish and they swallowed their words: "Suh." My tutor answered: "Ol' buddy!" Then they sat down. They didn't say a word to ask who I was, but one of them looked at Matorral, opened up his mouth and stuck out his lower lip in my direction. My preceptor gave his answer to this by stroking his beard and looking down at the floor. As soon as they saw that they jumped up in glee. They put their arms around me and began to slap me on the back. I did the same to them; it was like sampling four brands of wine. Time came to have dinner. A couple of big devils which toughs call *cañones* came over to the table to wait on us. We all sat down together. A roast capon made its appearance and my friends—to make me welcome—began to drink toasts to my honor. Until I saw all the toasting they did, I had no idea I had so much honor. Then in came platters of fish and meat, all prepared to stimulate thirst. There was a tub of wine on the floor and anyone who wanted a drink could bend right over and have his fill. I was just as happy with a bottle myself. After a couple of helpings, not one knew the other. They began to tell war stories. One swore louder than the other. From this toast to the next, twenty or thirty enemy dropped dead without so much as confession. They prescribed treatment of one thousand stabs for the Seville chief of police. They spoke reverently in memory of Domingo Tiznado, and they poured out a heady libation for the soul of the killer Escamilla. Some of my friends became weepy and cried tenderly over the late unlucky Alonso Alvarez. With all this reminiscing, the wheels in the head of my friend began ticking in bad time and he said rather hoarsely, taking up some bread in both hands and looking up at the light: "By this bread, which is the face of God, and by that light which came forth from the mouth of the angel, if you will, let us give the constable what he gave poor old One-eye." A huge shout arose among them. They took out their daggers, and putting their hands in the edge of the wine tub, swore:

"As we now drink this wine, so shall we drink the blood of all who try to catch us."

"Just who is this Alonso Alvarez," I asked, "for you to take his death so much to heart?"

"A fine young man," one of them said, "a brave fighter, always ready to give a hand, and a good companion. Let's go. The devils are plaguing me again."

"With that we left the house to go hunting for cops. I had

already capitulated to the wine and under its influence had renounced my common sense. Consequently I didn't realize what danger I was getting into. We got to La Mar Street where we ran right into the night watch. No sooner did we sight them than we drew our swords and rushed to the attack. I followed suit, and at the very first encounter we cleansed two of the cops of their damnable souls. The head constable told his men to take to their heels and ran up the street yelling for help. They had too good a head start for us to catch them. Eventually we took sanctuary in the cathedral where we were protected from the rigors of justice, and we slept long enough to evaporate the wine that boiled around in our skulls. When we came to, I could hardly believe that two cops had been killed and the chief chased off by a branch of the vine, for that is what we were. We had quite a good time in the church, as a group of lovable nymphs smelled out our refuge and took off their clothes to give us cover. One named La Grajal took to me, and I to her. This life was better and best of any I had ever known. As a consequence, I proposed to sail the seas of love with La Grajal till death do us part. I studied up on thieves' ballads and soon was cantor to my whole troupe of thugs. The police didn't give up the search for us; they prowled around outside the doors, but despite that, we got out after midnight and prowled around ourselves in disguise.

Seeing how long all this business was going on and that fortune persisted in harassing me—not that I was learning from experience, for I'm not that sensible, but, like the stubborn sinner I am, from sheer fatigue—I made up my mind, after talking it over with La Grajal, to sail for the New World with her and there to see if a change of continents would better my luck. It turned out to be worse, as you will see, sir, in the second part,* for a man who only changes his habitat and not his way of living never betters things for himself.

* No second part ever appeared.